Industrial
Mechanics

Third Edition

Workbook

AMERICAN TECHNICAL PUBLISHERS
ORLAND PARK, ILLINOIS 60467-5756

W9-BWC-845

Microsoft, Windows, Windows Vista, PowerPoint, and Internet Explorer are either registered trademarks or trademarks of Microsoft Corporation in the United States and/or other countries. Adobe, Acrobat, and Reader are registered trademarks of Adobe Systems Incorporated in the United States and/ or other countries. Intel is a registered trademark of Intel Corporation in the United States and/or other countries. Firefox is a registered trademark of the Mozilla Foundation. National Electric Code® (NEC®), and NEC are registered trademarks of the National Fire Protection Association, Inc. MasterFormat is a registered trademark of The Construction Specifications Institute, Inc. Vise-Grip is a registered trademark of American Tool Companies, Inc. Teflon is a registered trademark of E. I. Du Pont de Nemours and Company. QUAD-RING is a registered trademark of Quadion. FlukeView is a registered trademark of Fluke Corporation. Quick Quiz, Quick Quizzes, and Master Math are either registered trademarks or trademarks of American Technical Publishers, Inc.

3 4 5 6 7 8 9 – 12 – 9 8 7 6 5 4 3 2

Printed in the United States of America

ISBN 978-0-8269-3706-3

This book is printed on recycled paper.

Industrial Mechanics
WORKBOOK

CONTENTS

Industrial Mechanics Workbook is designed to reinforce the concepts in *Industrial Mechanics*. When studying the textbook, focus on italicized terms, illustrations, and examples. These key elements comprise a major portion of the workbook.

Review Questions

The workbook contains sections of Review Questions that contain a series of true-false, multiple choice, completion, and identification questions based on the text and illustrations in the corresponding chapter of the textbook. Study the assigned chapter of the textbook thoroughly before completing the Review Questions.

Problems

The workbook contains Problems developed from the chapters of the textbook. Problems provide opportunities to apply the concepts and theory in the textbook to practical mechanical and troubleshooting problems. Most Problem solutions require the application of basic math skills.

Final Exam

The Final Exam is developed from selected Review Questions from each of the chapters. The Final Exam is designed to test basic knowledge of mechanics, industrial systems, and troubleshooting.

Appendix

The comprehensive Appendix contains many useful tables, charts, and other supplemental reference material that is helpful when students develop solutions for each of the Problems, begin working in industrial facilities, and continue learning with on-the-job training. See page 153 for a complete listing of material in the Appendix.

Related Information

Information presented in *Industrial Mechanics* and *Industrial Mechanics Workbook* addresses common mechanical topics for several types of industrial systems. Answers to the workbook Review Questions and Problems are provided in the *Industrial Mechanics Answer Key*. *Industrial Mechanics* is one of many high-quality training products available from American Technical Publishers, Inc. To obtain information about related training products, visit the American Tech website at www.go2atp.com.

The Publisher

Name _____ Date _____

True-False

T   F   **1.** An accident victim does not need to provide consent before care is administered.

T   F   **2.** Safety shoes with reinforced steel toes provide protection against injuries caused by compression and impact.

T   F   **3.** The PPE selected must ensure a level of protection greater than the minimum level required to protect a technician from the hazard.

T   F   **4.** If a quart or more of blood is lost quickly, shock and/or death is possible.

T   F   **5.** Push tools rather than pulling them for greater control and balance.

T   F   **6.** Materials used in whole-body PPE include rubber, leather, synthetics, and plastic.

T   F   **7.** A personal fall-arrest system must be rigged so the technician cannot fall more than 6′.

T   F   **8.** A standard is a regulation or minimum requirement.

T   F   **9.** Individuals suffering from heat stroke may feel disoriented, feel dizzy, feel fatigued, have a headache, or have flu-like symptoms.

T   F   **10.** First aid is help for a victim after professional medical help arrives.

Multiple Choice

_____ **1.** Proper personal fall-arrest systems must be used when working at heights greater than ___′.
    A. 6
    B. 8
    C. 10
    D. 12

_____ **2.** ___ are the second most common cause of accidents, accounting for 35% of nonfatal injuries and 21% of over-three-day injuries.
    A. Slips and falls
    B. Improper lifting and moving
    C. Heat-related illnesses
    D. Poisoning and choking

_____ **3.** ___ are the only effective type of eye protection from nuisance dust because they create a protective seal around the eyes.
    A. Safety glasses
    B. Safety goggles
    C. Side shields
    D. Face shields

_____ **4.** A ___ is an accepted reference or practice.
    A. code
    B. standard
    C. regulation
    D. law

_____ **5.** A ___ space is a space large enough for an individual to physically enter and perform assigned work but has limited or restricted means for entry and exit and is not designed for continuous occupancy.
    A. restricted
    B. restrained
    C. contained
    D. confined

_____ **6.** Symptoms of shock include ___.
    A. warm, sweaty skin
    B. unusual hunger
    C. confusion
    D. all of the above

_____ **7.** Common sources of ___ include rotating equipment that has meshing gear teeth, chains and sprockets, rollers, belts, and pulleys.
    A. pinch points
    B. severe abrasions
    C. back injuries
    D. muscle cramps

_____ **8.** Required respirators must be ___ approved and medical evaluation and training must be provided before use.
    A. OSHA
    B. NFPA
    C. PPE
    D. NIOSH

_____ **9.** For burns caused by heat or chemicals, the burn should be immediately flushed with cool water for a minimum of ___ min.
- A. 10
- B. 20
- C. 30
- D. 40

_____ **10.** A ___ is a flexible line of rope, wire rope, or strap that generally has a connector at each end for connecting a body harness to a deceleration device, lifeline, or anchorage point.
- A. lanyard
- B. rope grab
- C. sling
- D. all of the above

_____ **11.** Checklist items required by OSHA for a confined space entry permit include the ___.
- A. permit expiration
- B. supervisor name
- C. rescue procedures
- D. all of the above

_____ **12.** Symptoms of ___ include confusion, collapse, unconsciousness, dry mottled skin, and skin that is warm or hot to the touch.
- A. heat exhaustion
- B. heat stroke
- C. choking
- D. shock

_____ **13.** The electrical parts of the motor in a ___ power tool are provided with extra insulation to prevent electrical shock.
- A. single-grounded
- B. double-grounded
- C. single-insulated
- D. double-insulated

_____ **14.** When moving a load on a cart, the technician's body weight should be used while taking ___ steps.
- A. even, short
- B. even, long
- C. uneven, short
- D. uneven, long

_____ **15.** No more than 2 hr of unprotected exposure to a sound level of ___ dB is recommended per OSHA 29 CFR 1926.52 (D)(1)—*Occupational Noise Exposure*.
- A. 50
- B. 75
- C. 100
- D. 125

Completion

_____ 1. ___ occurs when food or a foreign object obstructs the throat and interferes with normal breathing.

_____ 2. ___ includes safety glasses, hard hat, leather gloves, steel-toe work boots, earplugs, ear muffs, welding helmets, fire-resistant clothing, and dust masks.

_____ 3. The ___ is the lowest concentration (air-fuel mixture) at which a gas can ignite.

_____ 4. A(n) ___ provides a secure point of attachment for lifelines, lanyards, or other deceleration devices.

_____ 5. Various states have enacted ___ laws to give legal protection to individuals who provide emergency care to accident victims.

_____ 6. ___ protect the heads of technicians by resisting penetration and absorbing the blow of an impact.

_____ 7. A(n) ___ is a compressible device inserted into the ear canal to reduce the level of noise reaching the eardrum.

_____ 8. ___ is the additional vertical distance a falling technician travels, excluding lifeline elongation and free-fall distance, before stopping, from the point at which the deceleration device begins to operate.

_____ 9. A(n) ___ is a net made of rope or webbing for catching and protecting a falling technician.

_____ 10. ___ confined spaces are spaces that have the potential to contain a hazardous atmosphere, contain a material that has the potential for engulfing an entrant, or contain any other recognized safety or health hazard.

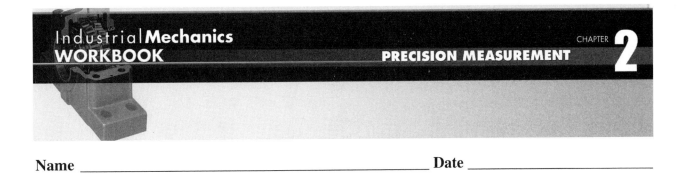

Name _____ **Date** _____

True-False

T   F   **1.** Digital calipers are more precise and easier to read than vernier or dial calipers but require a DC power source (battery) for operation.

T   F   **2.** An inside micrometer is a micrometer used for measuring outside diameters and thicknesses of parts.

T   F   **3.** A vernier scale is a short auxiliary scale placed along the main scale of an instrument to provide accurate fractional readings of the smallest division on the main scale.

T   F   **4.** Angles are measured in inches or centimeters.

T   F   **5.** A machinist's steel protractor is a tool used to measure or mark angle measurements on flexible, pliable workpieces.

T   F   **6.** Precision measuring instrument handling requires proper cleaning and lubrication of the instrument before and after each use.

T   F   **7.** Precision test instruments will not give faulty readings because of any expansion or contraction of the test instrument caused by temperature extremes.

T   F   **8.** An angle is a geometric figure formed by two lines extending from the same point.

T   F   **9.** An inside micrometer is a micrometer used to measure linear dimensions between two inside points or parallel surfaces.

T   F   **10.** Basic calibration of a depth micrometer requires that the measurement or rod extension start at one.

Multiple Choice

_____   **1.** A ___ is a permissible range of variation in a dimension or given value.
   A. variation
   B. tolerance
   C. rule
   D. none of the above

5

_____ **2.** Depth micrometers are used to measure distances of workpieces that have critical inside dimensions, such as ___.
    A. splines
    B. filter housings
    C. sleeve bearings
    D. all of the above

_____ **3.** ___ is the verification of graduations and incremental values of a precision measuring instrument for accuracy and adjustments.
    A. Tolerance
    B. Caliper adjustment
    C. Calibration
    D. Maintenance

_____ **4.** A ___ is a tool for measuring and laying out angles.
    A. caliper
    B. rule
    C. protractor
    D. micrometer

_____ **5.** Micrometers are used for verification of component dimensions such as ___.
    A. thickness
    B. diameter
    C. depth
    D. all of the above

_____ **6.** A(n) ___ is the fixed measuring surface of a micrometer.
    A. anvil
    B. thimble
    C. stop
    D. spindle

_____ **7.** A ___ is usually one tool with a combination of different measuring devices attached to a steel rule and is sometimes referred to as a combination square set.
    A. caliper
    B. rule
    C. protractor
    D. reversible protractor

_____ **8.** Conventional protractors are ___ in shape and have an outer scale, inner scale, zero edge, and center mark.
    A. circular
    B. semicircular
    C. rectangular
    D. oblong

_____ **9.** Depth micrometer measuring rod extensions typically vary by exactly ___″ and are calibrated by the set manufacturer.
    A. ¼
    B. ½
    C. 1
    D. 2

_____ **10.** ___ are designed with standard micrometer heads (thimble and barrel) attached to a flat "tee" base.
    A. Inside micrometers
    B. Outside micrometers
    C. Calipers
    D. none of the above

_____ **11.** On English vernier micrometers, the vernier scale can be used to measure as precisely as ___″.
    A. 0.01
    B. 0.001
    C. 0.0001
    D. 0.00001

_____ **12.** Digital calipers indicate digital readings in thousandths of an inch or ___ of a millimeter.
    A. tenths
    B. fiftieths
    C. hundredths
    D. thousandths

_____ **13.** A ___ micrometer has a printed anvil and spindle for measurement of grooves or keyways.
    A. ball
    B. disc
    C. point
    D. cup

_____ **14.** The metric system is based on divisions of ___.
    A. 1
    B. 5
    C. 10
    D. 20

_____ **15.** Common ___ used by tradesworkers are vernier, dial, and digital.
    A. protractors
    B. rules
    C. calipers
    D. none of the above

Completion

_____ 1. A(n) ___ is a tool designed to measure printed angles.

_____ 2. A(n) ___ is a straight line intersecting a point (vertex) of an angle.

_____ 3. A(n) ___ is a semiprecision measuring tool used for measuring length.

_____ 4. A(n) ___ micrometer is a micrometer with a digital electronic indicating gauge.

_____ 5. ___ is a method of using measuring instruments to acquire accurate measurements.

_____ 6. ___ are used to make precision inside diameter (ID), outside diameter (OD), and length measurements on components.

_____ 7. A(n) ___ angle is an angle exceeding 90°, but less than 180°.

_____ 8. A(n) ___ is a finely ground, precisely sized object that is used as a basis of dimensional comparison.

_____ 9. A(n) ___ is a precision-ground, moveable surface of a micrometer.

_____ 10. A(n) ___ fraction is a fraction with a denominator of 10, 100, 1000, etc.

Identification

Dial Calipers

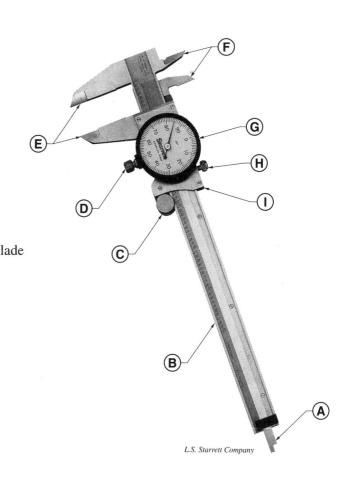

L.S. Starrett Company

_____ 1. Adjustment screw

_____ 2. Calibration screw

_____ 3. Depth measurement blade

_____ 4. Dial scale

_____ 5. Inside jaws

_____ 6. Locking screw

_____ 7. Main (beam) scale

_____ 8. Outside jaws

_____ 9. Sliding mechanism

Outside Micrometers

_____ **1.** Anvil

_____ **2.** Barrel

_____ **3.** Barrel scale

_____ **4.** Frame

_____ **5.** Spindle

_____ **6.** Spindle movement

_____ **7.** Stop

_____ **8.** Thimble

_____ **9.** Thimble rotation

_____ **10.** Thimble scale

_____ **11.** Vernier scale

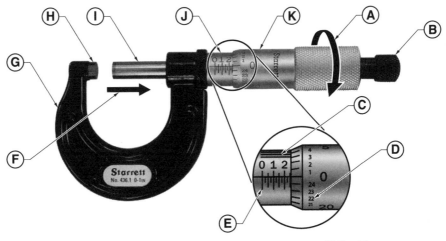

L.S. Starrett Company

Depth Micrometers

_____ **1.** Base

_____ **2.** Barrel

_____ **3.** Measured distance

_____ **4.** Rod

_____ **5.** Stop

_____ **6.** Thimble

_____ **7.** Zero point

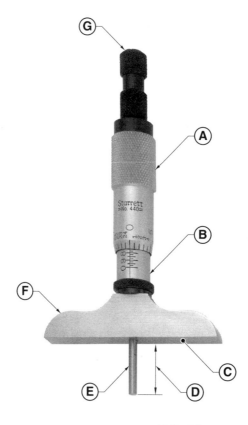

L.S. Starrett Company

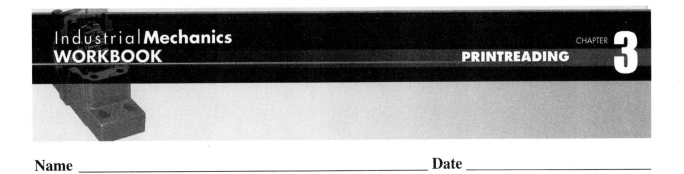
Name _____ **Date** _____

True-False

T   F   **1.** Foundation plans are used to determine the building materials that are used to build the main support structure.

T   F   **2.** Common architect's scales are rectangular in cross section and have six edges.

T   F   **3.** The two types of notes are general (construction) notes and sheet notes.

T   F   **4.** A break line is used to show a part's alternate positions or a repeated detail.

T   F   **5.** A head-on view is a view when looking directly at an object from the same height as the object.

T   F   **6.** A sectional drawing is a type of drawing that indicates the internal features of an object.

T   F   **7.** Typically, location drawings do not include dimensions.

T   F   **8.** A size dimension is a dimension that uses the components of an object to locate an angle or feature on an object.

T   F   **9.** Multiview sketches are three-dimensional representations of three-dimensional objects that are shown in true view.

T   F   **10.** A contour is an identifying outline that separates all or part of an object from the background.

Multiple Choice

_____   **1.** A floor plan is a plan view looking down at a building from approximately ___′ above the floor.
A. 5
B. 10
C. 50
D. 100

11

_____ **2.** A(n) ___ drawing is a type of drawing that is used to indicate how to do work using the simplest and/or safest method.
  A. assembly
  B. sectional
  C. instructional
  D. detail

_____ **3.** ___ plan designs include information about the landscaping that a specific piece of property can have.
  A. Floor
  B. Foundation
  C. Structural
  D. Utility

_____ **4.** A ___ is a reproduction of original drawings created by an architect or engineer.
  A. print
  B. plan
  C. legend sheet
  D. note

_____ **5.** ___ drawings are often used in installation and operational manuals to show where to connect external wires and position indicating lamps, switches, and displays.
  A. Application
  B. Orthographic
  C. Location
  D. none of the above

_____ **6.** Title block information typically includes ___.
  A. subject or sheet contents
  B. project title and location
  C. print division and print number
  D. all of the above

_____ **7.** A ___ drawing is a three-dimensional drawing that resembles a picture.
  A. head-on
  B. location
  C. detail
  D. pictorial

_____ **8.** ___ are used to locate the centers of windows, doors, and electrical enclosures and to indicate that an object is round or cylindrical in shape.
  A. Dimension lines
  B. Title blocks
  C. Centerlines
  D. all of the above

_____ **9.** General-purpose section lines are typically drawn ___″ apart at an incline of 45°.
    A. 1/32
    B. 1/16
    C. 1/10
    D. 1/8

_____ **10.** Underground utilities are commonly indicated with a ___ line or with a solid line that is broken for placement of a letter indicting the type of utility.
    A. dashed
    B. dotted
    C. dotted and dashed
    D. solid

_____ **11.** Small sets of prints are used for reference purposes and are usually either 8″ × 11″ or ___″ × ___″.
    A. 8, 10
    B. 8, 12
    C. 11, 17
    D. 11, 24

_____ **12.** A standalone symbol "×" on a print is an abbreviation for ___.
    A. centerline
    B. diameter
    C. radius
    D. repetitive feature

_____ **13.** ___ drawings show product use and are not intended to indicate component connections, wiring, dimensions, or actual size or shape.
    A. Location
    B. Detail
    C. Application
    D. none of the above

_____ **14.** A ___ plan is a drawing that shows exterior walls, all room partitions, doors, windows, furnaces, stairs, bathrooms, workspaces, and any fixtures or appliances.
    A. floor
    B. utility
    C. foundation
    D. structural

_____ **15.** Extension lines are drawn at ___° to the object and to the dimension lines.
    A. 45
    B. 60
    C. 75
    D. 90

Completion

_____ 1. A(n) ___ is a drawing that shows the property lines of a building lot, elevation, compass directions, lengths of property lines, and locations of structures.

_____ 2. A(n) ___ is a line that is used with a written dimension to indicate size or location.

_____ 3. A(n) ___ is a system of drawing representation in which drawing elements are proportional to actual elements.

_____ 4. All prints are composed of ___ to show the shape of the drawn object.

_____ 5. A(n) ___ is a block that identifies the changes that have been marked on the drawing since its initial approval.

_____ 6. A(n) ___ is a type of drawing where all faces of an object are projected onto flat planes that generally are at 90° angles to one another.

_____ 7. ___ plans are used to provide excavating, construction, drainage, water-proofing, and other design information for building the foundation.

_____ 8. A(n) ___ is an assembly of lines, dimensions, and notes used to convey general or specific information as required by the application and use.

_____ 9. A(n) ___ is a type of drawing that indicates the location of utilities such as electrical, water, sewage, gas, and communication cables.

_____ 10. A(n) ___ is additional information that is included with a set of prints.

_____ 11. A(n) ___ shows how the individual parts of an object work together.

_____ 12. Plans are two-dimensional drawings designed to indicate the ___ of objects.

_____ 13. The ___ is a nonprofit organization that provides standardized specifications for building construction.

_____ 14. ___ are often drawn freehand and without the use of technical instruments so that they can be used to quickly convey information visually when words may not give a complete description.

_____ 15. ___ is a method of adding dimensions to a drawing to indicate the geometrical characteristics of an object.

Identification

Section Line Types

_____ 1. Electrical windings, electromagnets, resistance, etc.

_____ 2. Marble, slate, glass, porcelain, ceramics

_____ 3. Cast iron, malleable iron, and general use for all materials

_____ 4. Wood

_____ 5. Magnesium, aluminum, and aluminum alloys

_____ 6. Steel

_____ 7. Rubber, plastic, and electrical insulation

_____ 8. Sound insulation

_____ 9. Titanium and refractory metal

_____ 10. Rock

_____ 11. Cork, felt, fabric, leather, and fiber

_____ 12. Earth

_____ 13. Sand

_____ 14. Concrete

_____ 15. Thermal insulation

_____ 16. Water and other liquids

_____ 17. Bronze, brass, copper

_____ 18. White metal, zinc, lead, babbitt, and alloys

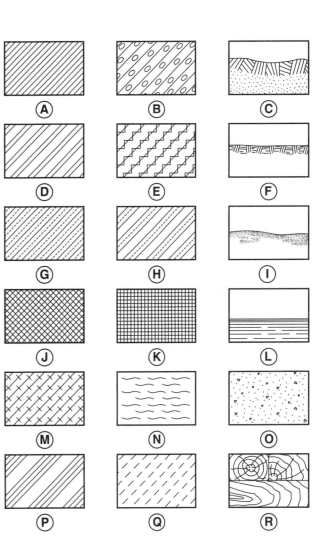

Line Types

1. Draw an object line.

2. What is an object line used for in prints?

3. Draw a phantom line.

4. What is a phantom line used for in prints?

5. Draw a hidden line.

6. What is a hidden line used for in prints?

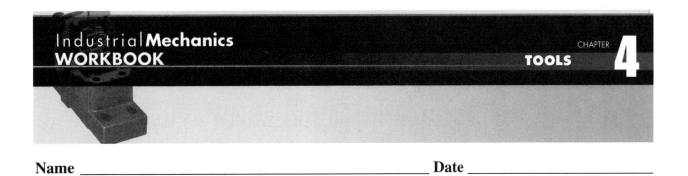

Name _____ **Date** _____

True-False

T   F   **1.** There are three main types of screwdrivers: flat head, Phillips head, and Allen.

T   F   **2.** Chisel types used for industrial and mechanical applications include flat cold, cape, round nose, and diamond point.

T   F   **3.** One of the guidelines for using hand tools for industrial applications is replacing damaged or worn tools as required.

T   F   **4.** Vises usually consist of a screw, lever, or cam mechanism that closes and holds two or more jaws around a workpiece.

T   F   **5.** High-quality handsaw blades should not be tapered from the blade top to the blade bottom.

T   F   **6.** External pullers are used to remove objects such as bearings or bushings from a bore.

T   F   **7.** Dies have a side with a 90° chamfer to prevent die-tooth breakage and to allow for a gentle cutting start.

T   F   **8.** Some types of power drills, such as hammer drills, can drill at speeds up to 3000 rpm and simultaneously hammer into the material at up to 50,000 blows per minute.

T   F   **9.** A circular saw is a multipurpose cutting tool in which the blade reciprocates to create the cutting action.

T   F   **10.** A puller is a tool used to cut external threads on round rods.

Multiple Choice

_____   **1.** A common wrench used for industrial and mechanical applications is the ___ wrench.
  A. socket
  B. adjustable
  C. pipe
  D. all of the above

17

_____ **2.** ___ taps are used after a taper tap has been used to start a true and straight thread.
    A. Bottom
    B. Plug
    C. Die
    D. Wrench

_____ **3.** The main parts of a handsaw are the blade, teeth, back, and ___.
    A. chisel
    B. head
    C. handle
    D. none of the above

_____ **4.** Some ___ resemble reverse-threaded screws, while others resemble square tapered rods with chiseled edges.
    A. screw extractors
    B. vises
    C. tape rules
    D. mechanical pullers

_____ **5.** A ___ is a hand tool with a tip designed to fit into a screw head for fastening operations.
    A. handsaw
    B. vise
    C. screwdriver
    D. punch

_____ **6.** End-cutting pliers are used for cutting ___ close to the workpiece.
    A. wire
    B. nails
    C. rivets
    D. all of the above

_____ **7.** File parts include the point, edge, face, heel, and ___.
    A. handle
    B. head
    C. tang
    D. blade

_____ **8.** ___ are used with a tap wrench to "pull" the tap into a workpiece.
    A. Taps
    B. Pliers
    C. Files
    D. Mechanical pullers

_____ **9.** ___ dies are used for tough cutting and are designed with thicker cross sections than round dies to permit cleaning and rethreading of threads.
    A. Square
    B. Triangular
    C. Hexagonal
    D. Octagonal

_____ **10.** A ___-handle hacksaw is usually preferred for fine work.
       A. pistol
       B. straight
       C. wooden
       D. metal

_____ **11.** Single-cut files have a single set of teeth cut at an angle of ___° to ___°.
       A. 45, 90
       B. 65, 85
       C. 75, 85
       D. 75, 90

_____ **12.** An 18-point saw blade has larger teeth than a(n) ___-point saw blade.
       A. 8
       B. 10
       C. 16
       D. 20

_____ **13.** Reciprocating saws typically operate at ___ to ___ strokes per minute (at no load).
       A. 1200, 1800
       B. 1500, 2500
       C. 1700, 2800
       D. 1800, 2900

_____ **14.** A ___ chisel is a chisel with a thin, tapered face and a narrow cutting edge.
       A. cape
       B. flat cold
       C. round-nose
       D. diamond-point

_____ **15.** Power tools use power from ___ power sources.
       A. electric
       B. pneumatic
       C. hydraulic
       D. all of the above

Completion

_____ **1.** A(n) ___ is a steel hand tool with one end formed to a conical point of approximately 90°.

_____ **2.** A(n) ___ is used to smooth areas enclosed by an acute angle.

_____ **3.** A(n) ___ is a striking or splitting tool with a hardened head fastened perpendicular to a handle.

_____ **4.** Most ___ strip standard wire from AWG size 22 to AWG size 10 and solid wire from AWG size 18 to AWG size 8.

_____ **5.** Industrial and mechanical technicians use ___ for various gripping, turning, cutting, positioning, and bending operations.

_____ **6.** A(n) ___ is a tool used to remove fitted machine parts.

_____ **7.** ___ due to improper use of taps when cutting metal can cause the cutting edges of taps to chip, break, or shatter.

_____ **8.** A(n) ___ is a cut that is made against the direction of the wood grain and is made with full, even strokes at about a 45° angle.

_____ **9.** A(n) ___ is a tool used to remove studs, bolts, or screws broken below or near the surface of a workpiece.

_____ **10.** A(n) ___ punch can mark an object without the use of a hammer.

Identification

Circular Saw Blades

_____ **1.** Abrasive

_____ **2.** Carbide-tipped finish and trim

_____ **3.** Carbide-tipped framing/rip

_____ **4.** Carbide-tipped plywood/veneer

_____ **5.** Chisel-tooth combination

_____ **6.** Combination

_____ **7.** Metal-cutting

_____ **8.** Plywood/paneling

_____ **9.** Rip

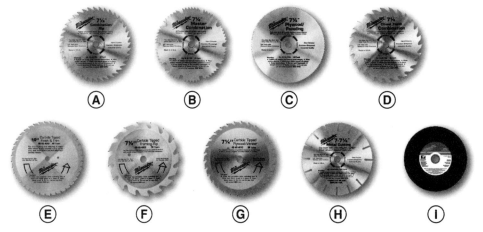

Milwaukee Electric Tool Corp.

Pliers

_____ 1. Diagonal-cutting

_____ 2. End-cutting

_____ 3. Lineman's

_____ 4. Locking

_____ 5. Long nose

_____ 6. Self-adjusting

_____ 7. Slip-joint

_____ 8. Tongue-and-groove

(A)

(B)

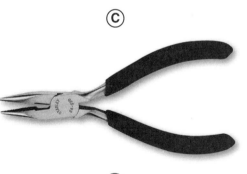

(C)

(D)

(E)

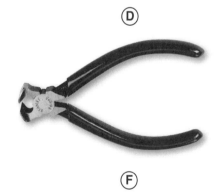
(F)

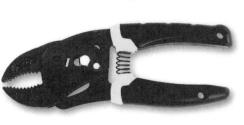
(G)

(H)

The Stanley Works

Punches

_____ **1.** Center

_____ **2.** Pin

_____ **3.** Prick

_____ **4.** Spring-loaded

_____ **5.** Solid

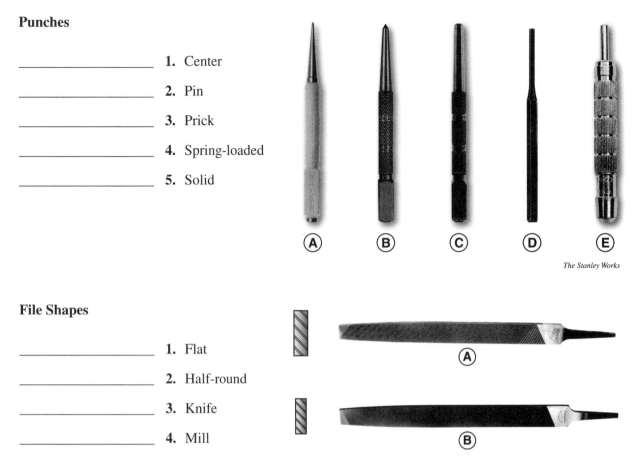

The Stanley Works

File Shapes

_____ **1.** Flat

_____ **2.** Half-round

_____ **3.** Knife

_____ **4.** Mill

_____ **5.** Round

_____ **6.** Square

_____ **7.** Three-square

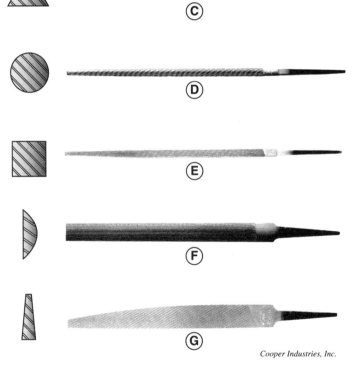

Cooper Industries, Inc.

Short Answer

1. Describe applications where a flat file is typically used.

2. Describe the procedure for removing a broken bolt or screw with a screw extractor.

3. The tap-drill size for a ½″-22 threaded hole is ___″.

4. Describe the procedure for cutting external threads by hand with a single-piece die.

5. Describe the procedure for cutting material by hand with a handsaw.

Name _____ Date _____

True-False

  T   F   **1.** All circles contain 360°.

  T   F   **2.** The sum of the three angles of a triangle is always 90°.

  T   F   **3.** A right cylinder is a cylinder with the axis perpendicular to the base.

  T   F   **4.** A formula can be changed to solve for any unknown value if the other values are known.

  T   F   **5.** A square foot contains 12 sq in.

  T   F   **6.** A polyhedron is any of a variety of solids bound by plane surfaces.

  T   F   **7.** There are 60′ in one degree.

  T   F   **8.** A straight angle always contains 90°.

  T   F   **9.** All lines may be drawn in any position, unless they are horizontal or vertical.

  T   F   **10.** Polygons are named according to their number of sides.

  T   F   **11.** A right triangle has a 3-4-5 relationship.

  T   F   **12.** In a formula, the sign of a number or letter is changed to the opposite sign when transposed.

  T   F   **13.** Angles are measured in degrees, minutes, and seconds.

  T   F   **14.** Supplementary angles are two angles formed by three lines in which the sum of the two angles equals 90°.

  T   F   **15.** A chord is a line from circumference to circumference through the centerpoint of a circle.

  T   F   **16.** A sector is a pie-shaped piece of a circle.

  T   F   **17.** The English system is the most common measurement system in the world.

  T   F   **18.** Pyramids are named according to the kind of polygon forming the base.

T   F   **19.** A right triangle is a triangle that contains one 90° angle and two equal sides.

T   F   **20.** Trapezoids and trapeziums are parallelograms.

Multiple Choice

_____ **1.** A quadrilateral always ___.
    A. has four sides
    B. contains 360°
    C. both A and B
    D. none of the above

_____ **2.** A ___ is a quadrilateral with opposite sides equal and four 90° angles.
    A. square
    B. rectangle
    C. rhombus
    D. rhomboid

_____ **3.** A ___ is a quadrilateral with all sides equal and no 90° angles.
    A. square
    B. rectangle
    C. rhombus
    D. rhomboid

_____ **4.** A(n) ___ is a regular solid of eight triangles.
    A. hexahedron
    B. octahedron
    C. tetrahedron
    D. dodecahedron

_____ **5.** A(n) ___ is a regular solid of twelve pentagons.
    A. hexahedron
    B. octahedron
    C. tetrahedron
    D. dodecahedron

_____ **6.** A(n) ___ is a regular solid of six squares.
    A. hexahedron
    B. octahedron
    C. tetrahedron
    D. dodecahedron

_____ **7.** ___ angles are two angles formed by three lines in which the sum of the two angles equals 90°.
    A. Acute
    B. Complementary
    C. Obtuse
    D. Right

_____ **8.** ___ angles have the same vertex and one side in common.
    A. Adjacent
    B. Chord
    C. Concentric
    D. Tangent

_____ **9.** The ___ is the boundary of a circle.
    A. arc
    B. circumference
    C. diameter
    D. radius

_____ **10.** The circumference of a 47″ D circle is ___″.
    A. 73.83
    B. 147.65
    C. 173.50
    D. 295.31

_____ **11.** The circumference of a 47″ R circle is ___″.
    A. 147.65
    B. 173.50
    C. 295.31
    D. 1734.95

_____ **12.** The area of a 35″ D circle is ___ sq in.
    A. 54.98
    B. 240.53
    C. 962.12
    D. 3848.45

_____ **13.** The area of a triangle with a 12″ base and a 15″ height is ___ sq in.
    A. 13.5
    B. 27
    C. 90
    D. 180

_____ **14.** The ___ is the point of intersection of the sides of an angle.
    A. centerpoint
    B. radius
    C. vertex
    D. none of the above

_____ **15.** A(n) ___ line is a line that is perpendicular to the horizon.
    A. horizontal
    B. vertical
    C. inclined
    D. none of the above

_____ **16.** An acute angle is an angle that ___.

A. contains less than 90°

B. contains exactly 90°

C. contains more than 90°

D. may contain any number of degrees

_____ **17.** A ___ is a portion of the circumference of a circle.

A. vector

B. chord

C. segment

D. none of the above

_____ **18.** Concentric circles are two or more circles with ___.

A. same diameters and same centerpoints

B. same diameters and different centerpoints

C. different diameters and same centerpoint

D. different diameters and different centerpoints

_____ **19.** Eccentric circles are two or more circles with ___.

A. same diameters and same centerpoints

B. same diameters and different centerpoints

C. different diameters and same centerpoint

D. different diameters and different centerpoints

_____ **20.** A cubic inch measures ___ or its equivalent.

A. 1″

B. 1″ sq

C. 1″ × 1″

D. none of the above

_____ **21.** An obtuse triangle is a scalene triangle with ___.

A. one angle less than 90°

B. one angle of 90°

C. one angle greater than 90°

D. two angles of 90°

_____ **22.** A polygon is ___.

A. a many-sided plane figure

B. bound by straight lines

C. both A and B

D. none of the above

_____ **23.** A trapezoid is a quadrilateral with ___ sides parallel.

A. no

B. two

C. opposite

D. all

_____ **24.** The circumference of a sphere is equal to the circumference of a ___ circle.
    A. great
    B. small
    C. either A or B
    D. none of the above

_____ **25.** An acute triangle is a(n) ___ triangle with each angle less than 90°.
    A. right
    B. isosceles
    C. equilateral
    D. scalene

Completion

_____ **1.** A(n) ___ is a means of showing that two numbers or two groups of numbers are equal to the same amount.

_____ **2.** A(n) ___ figure is a flat figure with no depth.

_____ **3.** A(n) ___ is the intersection of two lines or sides.

_____ **4.** The ___ of a prism is the perpendicular distance between the two bases.

_____ **5.** A(n) ___ is a solid generated by a circle revolving about one of its axes.

_____ **6.** A(n) ___ is a mathematical equation that contains a fact, rule, or principle.

_____ **7.** ___ is the number of unit squares equal to the surface of an object.

_____ **8.** The ___ of a triangle is the side upon which the triangle stands.

_____ **9.** A(n) ___ is a quadrilateral with all sides equal and four 90° angles.

_____ **10.** A(n) ___ is a quadrilateral with opposite sides equal and no 90° angles.

_____ **11.** A(n) ___ is a regular solid of four triangles.

_____ **12.** The prefix kilo (k) has a prefix equivalent of ___.

_____ **13.** A(n) ___ of a pyramid or cone is the remaining portion of a pyramid or cone with a cutting plane passed parallel to the base.

_____ **14.** The length of a hypotenuse of a triangle having sides of 23 m and 31 m is ___ m.

_____ **15.** The area of a 116′ × 54′ warehouse is ___ sq ft.

_____ **16.** The volume of a sphere that is 1′2″ in diameter is ___ cu ft.

_____ **17.** A(n) ___ is the boundary of a surface.

_____ **18.** A(n) ___ angle is two lines that intersect perpendicular to each other.

_____ **19.** A(n) ___ is a three-sided polygon with three interior angles.

_____ **20.** The ___ is the side of a right triangle opposite the right angle.

_____ **21.** The angles of a triangle are named by ___ letters.

_____ **22.** The sides of a triangle are named by ___ letters.

_____ **23.** A(n) ___ is a solid with two bases that are parallel and identical polygons.

_____ **24.** A(n) ___ is a solid with a base that is a polygon and sides that are triangles.

_____ **25.** ___ is the three-dimensional size of an object measured in cubic units.

Identification

Lines

_____ **1.** Line

_____ **2.** Straight line

_____ **3.** Horizontal line

_____ **4.** Vertical line

_____ **5.** Inclined line

_____ **6.** Parallel lines

A. Shortest distance between two points

B. Line that is slanted

C. Two or more lines that remain the same distance apart

D. Line that is perpendicular to the horizon

E. Line that is parallel to the horizon

F. Boundary of a surface

Angles

_____ **1.** Complementary

_____ **2.** Supplementary

_____ **3.** Right

_____ **4.** Straight

_____ **5.** Acute

_____ **6.** Obtuse

Circles

_____ **1.** Centerpoint

_____ **2.** Angle

_____ **3.** Chord

_____ **4.** Sector

_____ **5.** Diameter

_____ **6.** Semicircle

_____ **7.** Segment

_____ **8.** Radius

_____ **9.** Quadrant

_____ **10.** Arc

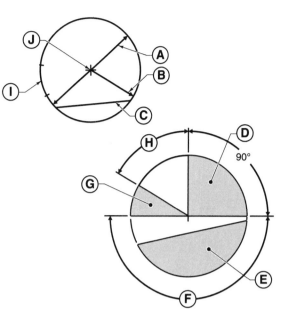

Polygons

_____ **1.** Quadrilateral

_____ **2.** Hexagon

_____ **3.** Heptagon

_____ **4.** Pentagon

_____ **5.** Octagon

_____ **6.** Triangle

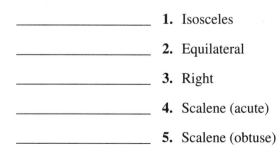

Triangles

_____ **1.** Isosceles

_____ **2.** Equilateral

_____ **3.** Right

_____ **4.** Scalene (acute)

_____ **5.** Scalene (obtuse)

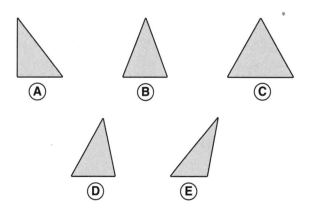

Pyramids

_____ **1.** Right rectangular

_____ **2.** Right triangular

_____ **3.** Oblique pentagonal

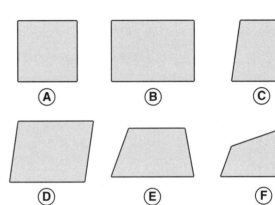

Quadrilaterals

_____ **1.** Trapezium

_____ **2.** Trapezoid

_____ **3.** Square

_____ **4.** Rectangle

_____ **5.** Rhombus

_____ **6.** Rhomboid

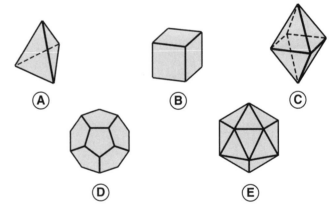

Regular Solids

_____ **1.** Icosahedron

_____ **2.** Dodecahedron

_____ **3.** Octahedron

_____ **4.** Tetrahedron

_____ **5.** Hexahedron

Other Regular Solids

_____ **1.** Oblate ellipsoid

_____ **2.** Prolate ellipsoid

_____ **3.** Torus

_____ **4.** Sphere

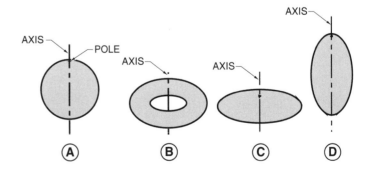

Conic Sections

_____ **1.** Circle

_____ **2.** Ellipse

_____ **3.** Parabola

_____ **4.** Hyperbola

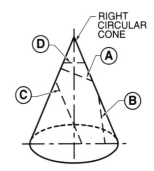

RIGHT CIRCULAR CONE

Problems

_____ **1.** The area of Circle A is ___ sq in.

_____ **2.** The area of Circle B is ___ sq ft.

_____ **3.** The circumference of Circle A is ___″.

_____ **4.** The circumference of Circle B is ___″.

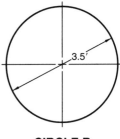

CIRCLE A   **CIRCLE B**

The piece of ⅛″ Rolled Steel is to be shear cut to produce 6″ × 8″ × 10″ triangular fins.

_____ **5.** The Rolled Steel has an area of ___ sq ft.

_____ **6.** The area of each triangular fin is ___ sq in.

_____ **7.** A total of ___ triangular fins can be produced from the Rolled Steel.

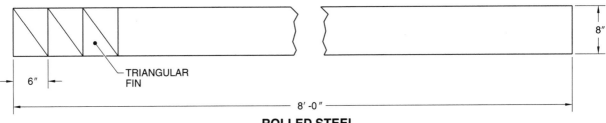

TRIANGULAR FIN

6″

8″

8′ -0″

ROLLED STEEL

_____ **8.** The Storage Tank will hold ___ cu ft of water.

_____ **9.** The Holding Tank, Storage Tank, and pipe will hold ___ cu ft of water.

_____ **10.** A 2′ D solid concrete ball placed in the Storage Tank will displace ___ cu ft of water.

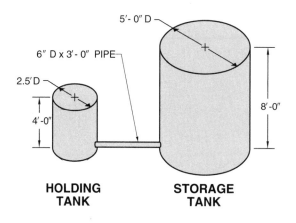

HOLDING TANK   **STORAGE TANK**

_____ **11.** The area of Rectangle A is ___ sq in.

RECTANGLE A

_____ **12.** The Warehouse contains ___ sq ft.

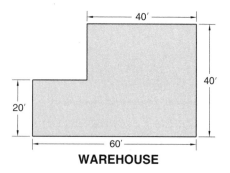

WAREHOUSE

_____ **13.** The circumference of Circle A is ___′.

_____ **14.** The area of Circle A is ___ sq ft.

_____ **15.** The area of Triangle A is ___ sq in.

_____ **16.** The length of Side c of Triangle A is ___″.

_____ **17.** The area of Circle B is ___ mm².

_____ **18.** The circumference of Circle B is ___ mm.

_____ **19.** A circle has a 28″ diameter. The area of the circle is ___ sq in.

_____ **20.** The Outer Zone contains ___ sq ft.

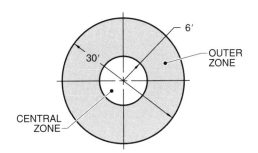

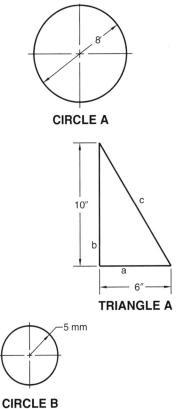

CIRCLE A

TRIANGLE A

CIRCLE B

_____ **21.** 2000 mg is equal to ___ dg.
  A. 0.02
  B. 0.2
  C. 2
  D. 200

_____ **22.** 800 gal. is equal to ___ l.
  A. 2998
  B. 3010
  C. 3019
  D. 3028

_____ **23.** 500 mi is equal to ___ km.
  A. 310
  B. 312.5
  C. 800
  D. 804.5

_____ **24.** 10,000 lb is equal to ___ kg.
       A. 3730
       B. 3932
       C. 4533
       D. 4540

_____ **25.** 36 in. is equal to ___ cm.
       A. 91.34
       B. 91.44
       C. 91.54
       D. 91.64

_____ **26.** 1500 l is equal to ___ kl.
       A. 0.15
       B. 1.5
       C. 15
       D. 150

_____ **27.** Seven tons is equal to ___ lb.
       A. 14,000
       B. 28,000
       C. 35,000
       D. 42,000

_____ **28.** One square mile is equal to ___ A.
       A. 330
       B. 640
       C. 950
       D. 1260

_____ **29.** 937 dal is equal to ___ l.
       A. 0.937
       B. 9.37
       C. 93.7
       D. 9370

_____ **30.** One metric ton is equal to ___ g.
       A. 10,000
       B. 100,000
       C. 1,000,000
       D. 10,000,000

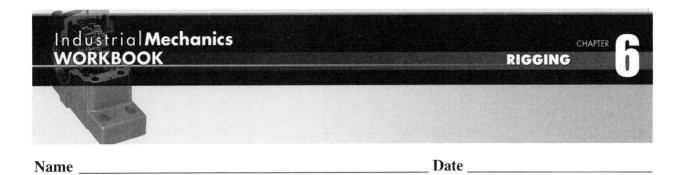

Name _____ Date _____

True-False

T	F	**1.**	The sling apex is the uppermost point where sling legs meet.
T	F	**2.**	Rope is used for lifting because of its length and flexibility.
T	F	**3.**	A socket is a rope attachment through which a rope end is terminated.
T	F	**4.**	Because a rope is flexible, bending does not subject it to stress.
T	F	**5.**	Fiber rope can be made from either natural or synthetic fibers.
T	F	**6.**	Wire rope with a fiber core should not be used in temperatures over 150°F.
T	F	**7.**	A scaffold hitch is made from a clove hitch and a bowline knot.
T	F	**8.**	The NACM specifies that the grade number or letter of a chain must appear at least once every 48 links.
T	F	**9.**	Hitches work by the pressure of rope being pressed together.
T	F	**10.**	A hitch is the interlacing of rope to temporarily secure it without knotting the rope.
T	F	**11.**	A bowline knot is a knot that forms a loop which slips along the rope from which it is made.
T	F	**12.**	A wagoner's hitch knot is a knot that creates a load-securing loop from the standing part of the rope.
T	F	**13.**	Webbing sling-strength capacity is rated for one-ply or two-ply in Class 5 or Class 7.
T	F	**14.**	Hoisting apparatus chain can be used in sling or lifting applications.
T	F	**15.**	A choker hook is a hook used to adjust or shorten a sling leg through the use of two chains.

Multiple Choice

_____ 1. A ___ is the interlacing of rope to form a permanent connection.
    A. hitch
    B. knot
    C. bight
    D. none of the above

_____ 2. ___ is a knitted or woven edge of a webbing formed to prevent raveling.
    A. Web ply
    B. Rebanding
    C. Selvedge
    D. Loop eye

_____ 3. Fiber rope is constructed by twisting ___.
    A. fibers into yarn
    B. yarn into strands
    C. strands into rope
    D. all of the above

_____ 4. A timber hitch is ___.
    A. a binding knot and hitch combination
    B. used to wrap and drag lengthy material
    C. either A or B
    D. none of the above

_____ 5. A ___ sling is created by slipping the loop from one end of the sling over the other end after wrapping the load.
    A. vertical
    B. choker
    C. basket
    D. bridle

Completion

_____ 1. ___ is securing equipment or machinery in preparation for lifting by means of wire rope slings, web slings, or chain.

_____ 2. A(n) ___ load is a load in which one-half of the load is a mirror image of the other half.

_____ 3. A lifting ___ is a thick metal loop (eyebolt) welded or screwed to a machine to allow balanced lifting.

_____ 4. Rope ___ is the length of rope in which a strand makes a complete helical wrap around the core.

_____ 5. A(n) ___ is any kind of a large class of sour substances with a pH value less than 7.

_____ **6.** A(n) ___ is a curved piece of metal around which the rope is fitted to form a loop.

_____ **7.** ___ is the process in which metal is brought to a temperature below its critical temperature and allowed to cool slowly.

_____ **8.** ___ strength is a metal's resistance to a force applied parallel to its contacted plane.

_____ **9.** A steel ___ is a metallic material formulated from the fusing or combining of two or more metals.

_____ **10.** ___ wire is a wire rope constructed of strands consisting of more than one size wire staggered in layers.

_____ **11.** A(n) ___ is the joining of two rope ends to form a permanent connection.

_____ **12.** The web sling ___ is the distance between the extreme points of a web sling, including any fittings.

_____ **13.** A(n) ___ is a U-shaped metal link with the ends drilled to receive a pin or bolt.

_____ **14.** Regarding wire rope, a strength safety factor of ___ is used for steady or even loads.

_____ **15.** ___ is hoisting equipment or machinery by mechanical means.

_____ **16.** A(n) ___ load is a load in which one-half of the load is not a mirror image of the other half.

_____ **17.** ___ is the balancing point of a load.

_____ **18.** The ___ weight center is a weight mass above a pivot point that causes a load to topple because it is top heavy.

_____ **19.** A(n) ___ is a line consisting of a strap, chain, or wire rope used to lift, lower, or carry a load.

_____ **20.** A(n) ___ is a bitter substance with a pH value greater than 7.

_____ **21.** ___ is the wrapping placed around all strands of a rope near the area where the rope is cut.

_____ **22.** ___ strength is a measure of the greatest amount of straight-pull stress metal can bear without tearing apart.

_____ **23.** ___ strength is a metal's resistance to deflection in the direction in which the load is applied.

_____ **24.** The diameter of wire rope is determined by the largest possible ___ dimension.

_____ **25.** ___ wire is wire rope that uses different size wire in different layers.

_____ **26.** ___ is a rope's attempt to rotate and untwist its strand lays while under stress.

_____ **27.** A(n) ___ is a complete helical wrap of the strands of a rope.

_____ **28.** A(n) ___ is a rope splice containing a thimble.

_____ **29.** The ___ of a web sling is a length of webbing folded back and spliced to the sling body, forming an opening.

_____ **30.** A(n) ___ pad is a leather or webbed pad used to protect the web sling from damage.

_____ **31.** A(n) ___ sling is a sling consisting of one or more continuous polyester fiber yarns wound together to make a core.

_____ **32.** A(n) ___ is a series of metal rings connected to one another and used for support, restraint, or transmission of mechanical power.

_____ **33.** Regarding wire ropes, a strength safety factor of ___ is used for uneven loads or lifts that may shock the slings.

_____ **34.** Basic web slings are fabricated in six configurations, which are ___ I through VI.

_____ **35.** ___ is the undesirable bending of a hook due to an applied force.

Identification

Webbing

_____ **1.** Tapered eye

_____ **2.** Loop eye length

_____ **3.** Eye width

_____ **4.** Sling width

_____ **5.** Web face

_____ **6.** Selvedge

_____ **7.** Splice

_____ **8.** Warning core

_____ **9.** Body

_____ **10.** Length

Hooks

_____ **1.** Swivel

_____ **2.** Gated

_____ **3.** Ungated

_____ **4.** Eye

_____ **5.** Clevis

Rigging Hardware Attachments

_____ **1.** Shackle

_____ **2.** Eyebolt

_____ **3.** Chain

_____ **4.** Hook

_____ **5.** Thimble

_____ **6.** Rope

_____ **7.** Clip

_____ **8.** Choker fitting

_____ **9.** Webbing

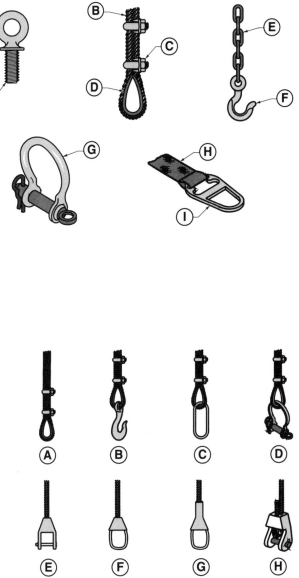

Wire Rope Terminations

_____ **1.** Wedge socket

_____ **2.** Open speltered socket

_____ **3.** Closed speltered socket

_____ **4.** Closed swaged socket

_____ **5.** Thimble

_____ **6.** Thimble and link

_____ **7.** Thimble and shackle

_____ **8.** Thimble and hook

Chain Inspection

_____ **1.** Bent links

_____ **2.** Cracks

_____ **3.** Stretching

_____ **4.** Excessive wear

_____ **5.** Gouges

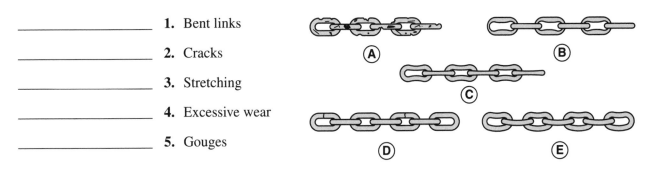

Rope Lay

_____ **1.** A(n) ___-lay is shown at A.

_____ **2.** A(n) ___-lay is shown at B.

_____ **3.** A(n) ___-lay is shown at C.

_____ **4.** A(n) ___-lay is shown at D.

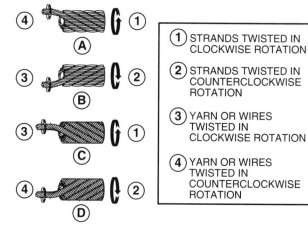

Rope Terminology

_____ **1.** Loop

_____ **2.** Kink

_____ **3.** Standing part

_____ **4.** Standing end

_____ **5.** Working part

_____ **6.** Whipping

_____ **7.** Bight

_____ **8.** Nip

_____ **9.** Eye loop

_____ **10.** Working end

Hoisting Hooks

_____ **1.** Foundry

_____ **2.** Choker

_____ **3.** Swivel

_____ **4.** Grab

_____ **5.** Sorting

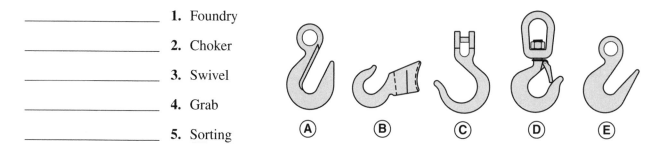

Basic Sling Combinations

_____ **1.** Basket

_____ **2.** Bridle

_____ **3.** Choker

_____ **4.** U

_____ **5.** Vertical (single-leg)

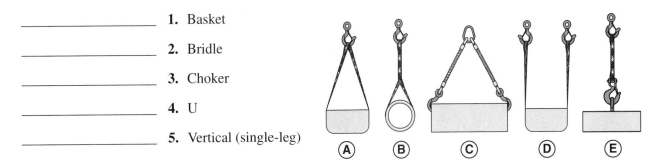

Ⓐ   Ⓑ   Ⓒ   Ⓓ   Ⓔ

Slings

_____ **1.** Type I

_____ **2.** Type II

_____ **3.** Type III

_____ **4.** Type IV

_____ **5.** Type V

_____ **6.** Type VI

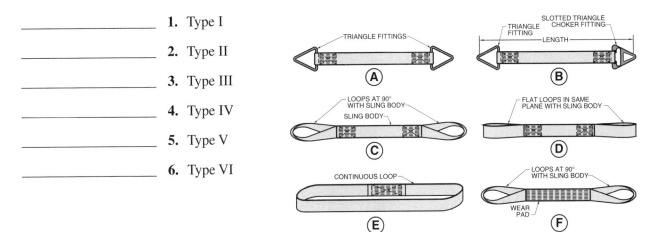

Problems

Refer to appropriate tables in Appendix.

_____ **1.** The pieces of 1¾″ D round steel weigh ___ lb.

_____ **2.** Three 10′ pieces of ¼″ D round steel and one 10′ piece of 1″ square steel weighs ___ lb.

_____ **3.** An order for twenty-four 36″ × 96″ sheets of ¼″ steel plate weighs ___ lb.

ROUND STEEL

_____ **4.** The loss factor is ___ if the sling angle is 50° from the horizon.

_____ **5.** The total lifting capacity of a two-leg sling made of ¼″, 6 × 19, IPS-FC wire rope with the sling loops constructed of swaged sockets and sling angles of 60° is ___ t.

_____ 6. The rope bending load rating of a ½″ rope traveling over an 8″ pulley with a load rating of 1800 lb is ___ lb.

_____ 7. The generally accepted safe wire rope strength to lift 5000 lb with a steady lift is ___.

_____ 8. The lifting capacity of a basket hitch using a 1½″ wide Class 5, Type V endless sling without fittings and having a 40° sling angle is ___ lb.

_____ 9. The lifting capacity of a round sling basket hitch with a yellow cover and 50° sling angle is ___ lb.

_____ 10. Should the used chain be removed from service?

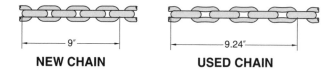

| ⟵——— 9″ ———⟶ | ⟵——— 9.24″ ———⟶ |
| **NEW CHAIN** | **USED CHAIN** |

_____ 11. The 10′ pieces of 1¼″ D brass weigh ___ lb.

_____ 12. Fifteen 10′ pieces of ¾″ D round steel and four 10′ pieces of 1″ square steel weigh ___ lb.

_____ 13. Twenty-eight 48″ × 96″ sheets of ¼″ steel plate weighs ___ lb.

10′

1¼″ D

BRASS

_____ 14. The loss factor is ___ if the sling angle is 65° from the horizon.

_____ 15. The total lifting capacity of a two-leg sling made of ⅜″, 6 × 19, IPS-FC wire rope with the sling loops constructed of wedged sockets and sling angles of 70° is ___ t.

_____ 16. The rope bending load rating of a ½″ rope traveling over a 6″ pulley with a load rating of 1500 lb is ___ lb.

_____ 17. The generally accepted safe wire rope strength to lift 3000 lb with a steady lift is ___.

_____ 18. The lifting capacity of a basket hitch using a 1½″ wide Class 5, Type V endless sling without fittings and having a 50° sling angle is ___ lb.

_____ 19. The lifting capacity of a round sling basket hitch with a tan cover and 45° sling angle is ___ lb.

_____ 20. Should the used chain be removed from service?

| ⟵——— 8″ ———⟶ | ⟵——— 8.08″ ———⟶ |
| **NEW CHAIN** | **USED CHAIN** |

Name _____ **Date** _____

True-False

T　　F　　**1.** The nominal breaking strength of the most heavily loaded rope in a system shall be no less than 2½ times the load applied to that rope.

T　　F　　**2.** Torque is the twisting (rotational) force of a shaft.

T　　F　　**3.** In a bevel gear, the drive gear is the smaller gear.

T　　F　　**4.** Ambient temperature is the temperature of the air surrounding a piece of equipment.

T　　F　　**5.** As a sling moves from a vertical to an angular position, the capacity of the eyebolt is increased.

T　　F　　**6.** A crane should be used for a side pull.

T　　F　　**7.** A crane operator takes signals only from the assistant, no exceptions.

T　　F　　**8.** Adjustable slip clutches must never be adjusted to hold over 125% of the hoist-rated load.

T　　F　　**9.** Hoist limit switches and other safety devices should be checked daily.

T　　F　　**10.** Monthly equipment checks are generally concerned with load-bearing components, such as the condition of hooks, wire rope, chain, and nut and bolt tightness.

Multiple Choice

_____ **1.** A ___ is a rope length between the lower (hook) block and the upper block or drum.
A. piece
B. part
C. portion
D. none of the above

_____ **2.** A ___ line is the part of the rope to which force is applied to hold or move a load.
A. load
B. lead
C. front
D. back

_____ **3.** The proper direction for winding the first layer of rope on a drum is determined by the ___ of the rope.
  A. length
  B. diameter
  C. lay
  D. none of the above

_____ **4.** A(n) ___ chain is the chain that raises the load.
  A. pull
  B. lift
  C. pickup
  D. hoist

_____ **5.** Hand-chain hoists are suspended overhead from a(n) ___ hook attached to a supporting structure.
  A. main
  B. overhead
  C. top
  D. master

_____ **6.** Lever-operated hoists are generally used to lift loads that weigh from ___ lb to ___ lb.
  A. 100; 300
  B. 200; 500
  C. 300; 600
  D. none of the above

_____ **7.** ___ provides a worldwide forum for the standards-developing process.
  A. OSHA
  B. ASME
  C. The ISO
  D. The NFPA

_____ **8.** A straight vertical pull of a shoulder nut eyebolt offers ___% of the eyebolt load rating.
  A. 85
  B. 90
  C. 95
  D. 100

_____ **9.** Three common ___ crane configurations are the top-running crane with top-running hoist, the top-running crane with underhung hoist, and the underhung crane with underhung hoist.
  A. overhead
  B. jib
  C. gantry
  D. none of the above

_____ **10.** A ___ is the rail and beam on which the crane operates.
      A. cantilever
      B. runway
      C. girder
      D. trolley

Completion

_____ **1.** ___ is the hoisting of equipment or machinery by mechanical means.

_____ **2.** Mechanical ___ is the ratio of the output force to the input force of a device.

_____ **3.** A(n) ___ is a pushbutton or lever control suspended from a crane or hoisting apparatus.

_____ **4.** The two basic types of eyebolts are formed steel and ___ steel.

_____ **5.** A(n) ___ is a bolt with a looped head.

_____ **6.** A(n) ___ is an assembly of hooks, pulleys, and a frame suspended by hoisting ropes.

_____ **7.** ___ is passing a rope through a hole or opening or around a series of pulleys.

_____ **8.** A(n) ___ is a mechanism used to prevent the ratchet wheel of a lever-operated hoist from turning backwards.

_____ **9.** A(n) ___ hoist is a power-operated hoist operated by a geared reduction air motor.

_____ **10.** Drum ___ is the rope length required to make one complete turn around the drum of a hoist or crane.

_____ **11.** Hook ___ is the slippage of a hook caused by insufficient braking.

_____ **12.** Typical eyebolt angular lift capacity is calculated using a constant of ___ for sling angles of less than 45°.

_____ **13.** A(n) ___ crane is a crane with bridge beams supported on legs.

_____ **14.** A(n) ___ crane is a crane with a boom constructed from a gridwork of steel reinforcing members.

_____ **15.** A(n) ___ is a projecting beam (boom) or member supported at only one end.

Identification

Drum Wrap

_____ **1.** Underwind left to right

_____ **2.** Overwind left to right

_____ **3.** Underwind right to left

_____ **4.** Overwind right to left

Safety

_____ **1.** OSHA

_____ **2.** ANSI

_____ **3.** ISO

_____ **4.** CMAA

_____ **5.** ASME

_____ **6.** NFPA

A. Publishes the National Electrical Code®, which contains standards for the practical safeguarding of persons and property from hazards arising from the use of electricity.

B. Nongovernmental international organization comprised of national standards institutions of over 90 countries.

C. U.S. standards-developing organization that adopts and co-publishes standards that are written and approved by member organizations.

D. U.S. government organization concerned with the development and enforcement of safety standards for industrial workers.

E. Oranization of crane manufacturers that promotes standardization and establishes crane-operating practice standards.

F. Organization that helps establish safe structural design of hoists and cranes and sets safety standards.

Crane Hand Signals

_____ **1.** Raise boom

_____ **2.** Lower boom

_____ **3.** Raise boom and lower load

_____ **4.** Lower boom and raise load

_____ **5.** Trolley travel

_____ **6.** Swing

_____ **7.** Stop

_____ **8.** Emergency stop

_____ **9.** Move slowly

_____ **10.** Tower travel

_____ **11.** Hoist

_____ **12.** Lower

_____ **13.** Use main hoist

_____ **14.** Use auxiliary hoist

Hand-Chain Hoists

_____ **1.** Hoist chain

_____ **2.** Lower limit of hoist hook travel

_____ **3.** Upper limit of hoist hook travel

_____ **4.** Hoist hook

_____ **5.** Reach

_____ **6.** Pocket wheel

_____ **7.** Top hook

_____ **8.** Hand chain

_____ **9.** Head room

_____ **10.** Lift

_____ **11.** Hand chain drop

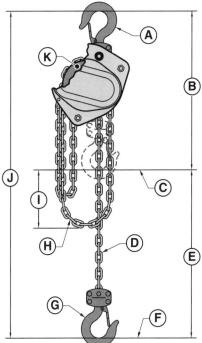

Jib Cranes

_____ **1.** Wall-mounted, top-braced

_____ **2.** Wall-mounted, cantilevered

_____ **3.** Mast, cantilevered

_____ **4.** Mast, underbraced

_____ **5.** Mast, top-braced

_____ **6.** Base-mounted, cantilevered

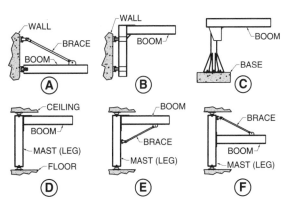

Problems

_____ 1. A force of ___ lb is required to hold a 600 lb load using a three-part reeving system.

_____ 2. Under ideal conditions, the lead line at A requires a pull of ___′ to lift the 100 lb load.

_____ 3. Under ideal conditions, the lead line at A requires a force of ___ lb to lift the 100 lb load.

_____ 4. A force of ___ lb is required to move an 8000 lb load using a 10-part reeving system equipped with rolling-contact bearing pulleys.

_____ 5. A(n) ___ lb force is required to move a 1000 lb load using one-part reeving and plain bearing pulleys.

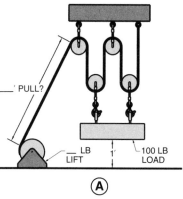

_____ 6. The minimum compressor size required for a pneumatic hoist that requires 110 scfm is ___ HP.

_____ 7. The working load capacity of a 40° bridle sling using a ⅝″ shoulder nut eyebolt is ___ lb.

_____ 8. The working load of a 60° bridle sling using a ¼″ shoulder nut eyebolt is ___ lb.

_____ 9. The minimum output of a compressor rated at 11 HP is ___ scfm.

_____ 10. The minimum output of a compressor rated at 7.5 HP is ___ scfm.

_____ 11. The percent change in eyebolt capacity of a sling that has been relocated from 81° to 58° is ___%.

_____ 12. A force of ___ lb is required to move a 30,200 lb load using a four-part reeving system with rolling-contact bearing pulleys.

_____ 13. A force of ___ lb is required to move a 21,925 lb load using a 15-part reeving system with plain bearing pulleys.

_____ 14. A shim thickness of ___″ is required for a 90° rotation of a 1¼″ eyebolt.

_____ 15. The working load capacity of a 40° bridle sling using a ½″ shoulder nut eyebolt is ___ lb.

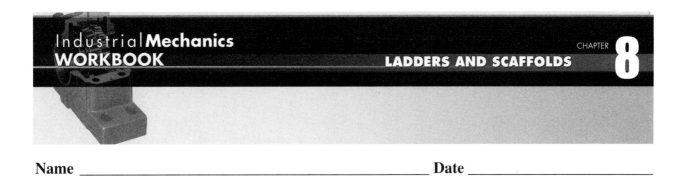

Name _____ **Date** _____

True-False

T   F   **1.** Fiberglass ladders conduct electricity when dry.

T   F   **2.** A fixed ladder is permanently attached to a structure.

T   F   **3.** Netting mesh size for bodily fall protection is normally 6″ × 6″.

T   F   **4.** Border rope for safety nets shall have a 2500 lb breaking strength when new.

T   F   **5.** A person should always face the ladder when ascending or descending.

T   F   **6.** Ladders are intended for use by only one person unless specifically designated otherwise.

T   F   **7.** Fixed ladders are commonly constructed of steel or aluminum.

T   F   **8.** Single ladders are of fixed length having only one section.

T   F   **9.** A mobile scaffold may be moved with a worker on the platform.

T   F   **10.** Foot pads are generally attached to long ladders such as extension ladders.

Multiple Choice

_____   **1.** A heavy-duty, industrial, 250 lb capacity ladder has a Type ___ rating.
   A. IA
   B. I
   C. II
   D. III

_____   **2.** Fixed ladders are installed in a preferred pitch range between ___° and 90° from horizontal.
   A. 45
   B. 60
   C. 75
   D. none of the above

51

_____ **3.** Guardrails on scaffolds must be installed no less than ___″ or more than ___″ high, with a midrail.

    A. 24; 30

    B. 30; 36

    C. 38; 45

    D. 42; 48

_____ **4.** Nails smaller than ___d common must not be used to construct scaffolds.

    A. 8

    B. 10

    C. 12

    D. 16

_____ **5.** A safety net must be used anywhere a person is working ___′ or more above ground, water, machinery, or any other solid surface when the worker is not otherwise protected by a lifeline, harness, or scaffolding.

    A. 10

    B. 25

    C. 40

    D. 60

_____ **6.** Stepladders are commonly ___ in length.

    A. 2′-0″ to 6′-0″

    B. 2′-0″ to 8′-0″

    C. 4′-0″ to 8′-0″

    D. 4′-0″ to 10′-0″

_____ **7.** The spacing between rungs of ladders, except for stepstools, shall be on ___″ centers ± ___″.

    A. 8; ⅛

    B. 8; ¼

    C. 12; ⅛

    D. 12; ¼

_____ **8.** A scaffold over ___′ in height must be securely guyed or tied to the structure or building with No. 12 double-wrapped wire.

    A. 10

    B. 15

    C. 20

    D. 25

_____ **9.** Fixed ladders over ___′ in length must have a cage, well, or ladder safety system.

    A. 10

    B. 12

    C. 24

    D. 30

_____ **10.** The tip of a single or extension ladder must be at least ___′ above the roof line or top support.

      A. 1

      B. 2

      C. 3

      D. 4

_____ **11.** Ladders over ___′ in height must be secured at the bottom.

      A. 8

      B. 10

      C. 12

      D. 15

_____ **12.** For fixed ladders using a ladder safety system, rest platforms must be provided at maximum intervals of ___′.

      A. 100

      B. 150

      C. 175

      D. 200

_____ **13.** The surface of a mobile scaffold must be within ___° of level.

      A. 1½

      B. 2

      C. 2½

      D. 3

_____ **14.** The advantages of ___ ladders include relatively low cost, ability to take abuse, nonconductivity of electricity, and good temperature insulating qualities.

      A. metal

      B. plastic

      C. wood

      D. none of the above

_____ **15.** Extension ladders are positioned on a ___ ratio (75° angle).

      A. 2:1

      B. 3:1

      C. 4:1

      D. 5:1

Completion

_____ **1.** Metal ladders should not be used within ___′ of electrical circuits or equipment.

_____ **2.** Most metal ladders are normally constructed of ___, which is a relatively light metal.

_____ **3.** A(n) ___ ladder is an adjustable-height ladder with a fixed bed section and sliding, lockable fly sections.

_____ **4.** All scaffolds ___′ or more above ground must have guardrails, midrails, and toeboards.

_____ **5.** A(n) ___ scaffold is a scaffold supported by overhead wire ropes.

_____ **6.** The maximum working height of a hydraulic scissor lift scaffold is ___′.

_____ **7.** Scaffold platform planks consist of ___″ nominal structural planks.

_____ **8.** A(n) ___ scaffold is a wood scaffold with one or two sides firmly resting on the floor or ground.

_____ **9.** The overlap of the fly section of a 42′ extension ladder shall be at least ___′.

_____ **10.** A(n) ___ is a rope used for hoisting or lowering objects.

_____ **11.** The minimum distance between the center of the rung of a fixed ladder to the building wall is ___″.

_____ **12.** A cage, well, or ladder safety system must be provided where a single length of climb on a fixed ladder is greater than 24′ but less than ___′.

_____ **13.** Ladder ___ rating is the weight (in lb) a ladder is designed to support under normal use.

_____ **14.** A Type ___ stepladder is designed for light-duty, household use.

_____ **15.** A(n) ___ is the track of a ladder safety system consisting of a flexible cable or rigid rail secured to the ladder or structure.

Identification

Sectional Metal-Framed Scaffolds

_____ **1.** Bearer

_____ **2.** Hook-on ladder

_____ **3.** Diagonal brace

_____ **4.** Cross brace

_____ **5.** Coupling tube

_____ **6.** Footing base plate

_____ **7.** Cleat

_____ **8.** Planking

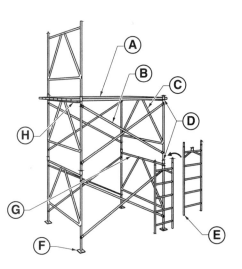

Ladder Jacks

_____	**1.**	Hook
_____	**2.**	Ladder jack
_____	**3.**	Ladder
_____	**4.**	Plank
_____	**5.**	Hook

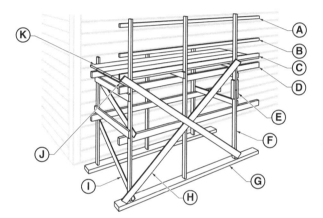

Pole Scaffolds

_____	**1.**	Ledger
_____	**2.**	Cross brace
_____	**3.**	Diagonal brace
_____	**4.**	Planking
_____	**5.**	Footing
_____	**6.**	Guardrail
_____	**7.**	Upright
_____	**8.**	Midrail
_____	**9.**	Toeboard
_____	**10.**	Bearer
_____	**11.**	Splice

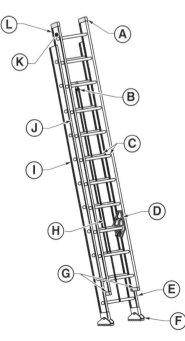

Extension Ladders

_____	**1.**	Halyard
_____	**2.**	Rungs
_____	**3.**	Tip
_____	**4.**	Butt end
_____	**5.**	Plastic rail closures
_____	**6.**	Center swivel pulley
_____	**7.**	Foot assembly
_____	**8.**	Flange
_____	**9.**	Web
_____	**10.**	Bed section
_____	**11.**	Pawl lock
_____	**12.**	Fly section

Pawl Locks

_____ **1.** The fly section of the ladder at ___ is held in place.

_____ **2.** The fly section of the ladder at ___ is being lowered.

_____ **3.** The fly section of the ladder at ___ is being raised.

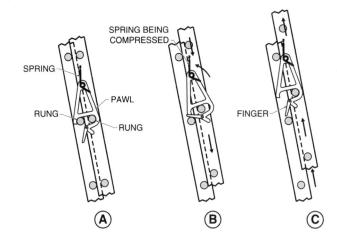

Problems

_____ **1.** An extension ladder has a working height of 16′. The butt end of the ladder is placed ___′ from the wall.

_____ **2.** A 54′ extension ladder shall have an overlap of at least ___′.

_____ **3.** The braces of a medium-duty single-pole scaffold shall be constructed of ___ material.

_____ **4.** Rails for light-duty double-pole scaffolds shall be constructed of ___ material.

_____ **5.** The base of a metal-framed scaffold measures 6′ × 12′. The maximum height of the scaffold is ___′.

_____ **6.** The minimum base dimension of the Mobile Scaffold is ___′.

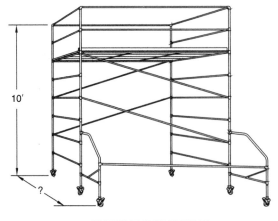

MOBILE SCAFFOLD

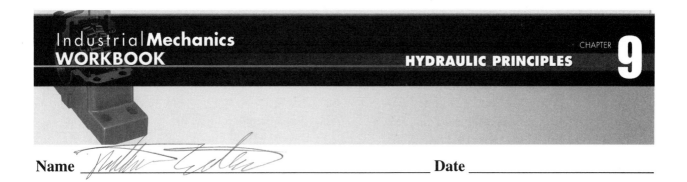

Name _____ Date _____

True-False

T **F**   **1.** Area, force, and pressure are the basis of all hydraulic systems.

T F   **2.** The pressure of the fluid at any level in a vessel is the same regardless of the shape of the vessel.

T **F**   **3.** Fluids that are thin and flow easily have a high viscosity.

T **F**   **4.** One gallon of fluid equals 321 cu in.

T F   **5.** The velocity of a fluid decreases as the cross-sectional area of a pipe increases.

T **F**   **6.** Mineral-base oil is the most widely used hydraulic fluid.

T **F**   **7.** Static head pressure is potential energy.

T **F**   **8.** Volume is the two-dimensional size of an object measured in cubic units.

T F   **9.** Flow rate is the volume of fluid flow.

T **F**   **10.** Static energy is the energy of motion.

T F   **11.** Any friction generated in a hydraulic system becomes a resistance to fluid flow.

T **F**   **12.** The velocity of a fluid is constant from one moment to another as its speed or direction of flow changes.

T F   **13.** Total energy is a measure of a fluid's ability to do work.

T F   **14.** Head is the difference in the level of a liquid between two points.

T **F**   **15.** Fluids that flow with difficulty have a low viscosity.

T **F**   **16.** Capacity is expressed in square units.

T **F**   **17.** In an open cylinder, the pressure of a fluid at any depth in the cylinder is proportional to the width of the fluid column.

T F   **18.** Less hydraulic fluid is required to retract a piston than is required to extend a piston.

T   F   **19.** Acceleration is constantly changing within a hydraulic system.

T   F   **20.** The speed of a cylinder rod is dependent on pressure.

Multiple Choice

_____ C _____ **1.** One horsepower is the amount of energy required to lift ___ lb 1′ in 1 min.
A. 330
B. 550
C. 33,000
D. 55,000

_____ C _____ **2.** ___ is the height at which atmospheric pressure forces a fluid above the elevation of its supply source.
A. Increase
B. Elevation
C. Lift
D. none of the above

_____ C _____ **3.** In a hydraulic system ___.
A. pressure provides force
B. flow rate provides speed
C. both A and B
D. neither A nor B

_____ A _____ **4.** Area is always expressed in ___ units.
A. square
B. cubic
C. either A or B
D. neither A nor B

_____ B _____ **5.** ___ lift is the lift of fluid in motion.
A. Static
B. Dynamic
C. Head
D. none of the above

_____ B _____ **6.** ___ is the rate or speed of doing work.
A. Energy
B. Power
C. Capacity
D. Efficiency

_____ B _____ **7.** The viscosity ___ is a scale used to show the magnitude of viscosity changes in lubrication oils with changes in temperature.
A. rate
B. index
C. time
D. temperature

_____ C _____ **8.** ___ head is the head of fluid in motion.
   A. Static
   B. Still
   C. Dynamic
   D. Divergent

_____ B _____ **9.** ___ is the volume of hydraulic fluid moved during each revolution of a pump's shaft.
   A. Residue
   B. Displacement
   C. Load
   D. none of the above

_____ C _____ **10.** ___ is a measure of a component's or system's useful output energy compared to its input energy.
   A. Rate
   B. Percentage
   C. Efficiency
   D. Value

_____ B _____ **11.** The amount of pressure required to move a 6800 lb force with a 6″ D piston is ___ psi.
   A. 240
   B. 240.5
   C. 241
   D. 241.5

_____ B _____ **12.** The area of a circle with a diameter of 4.275″ is ___ sq in.
   A. 4.57
   B. 14.35
   C. 16.08
   D. 18.28

_____ C _____ **13.** The absolute pressure in a system under standard conditions with a gauge reading of 212 psig is ___ psia.
   A. 212.49
   B. 213.47
   C. 226.70
   D. 241.92

_____ A _____ **14.** The pressure at the base of a 55 gal. polyethylene drum with an inside diameter of 23½″ and a height of 36¼″ filled with kerosene is ___ lb/sq in.
   A. 1.07
   B. 1.10
   C. 1.17
   D. 1.73

_____ B _____ **15.** The velocity of cold water flowing at 100 gpm through a 60″ section of 3″ D galvanized pipe is ___ ft/sec.
   A. 1.63
   B. 4.54
   C. 19.62
   D. 40.62

_____C_____ **16.** The rod speed of a 9.1 gpm multistage booster pump with a 4″ D cylinder is ___ in./min.
    A. 18.38
    B. 94.31
    C. 167.23
    D. 320.83

_____C_____ **17.** The amount of horsepower required to move a 20,380 lb steel coil 100′ in 45 sec is ___ HP.
    A. 8.24
    B. 22.04
    C. 82.34
    D. 102.74

_____C_____ **18.** A barometric pressure of ___″ Hg equals one atmosphere.
    A. 0.7854
    B. 14.7
    C. 29.92
    D. 34.4

_____A_____ **19.** ___ is the height of a fluid above a given point in a column at rest.
    A. Static head
    B. Dynamic head
    C. Static lift
    D. Dynamic lift

_____B_____ **20.** Volumetric efficiency is the percentage of actual pump output compared to the pump output if there were no ___.
    A. friction
    B. slippage
    C. viscosity
    D. none of the above

Completion

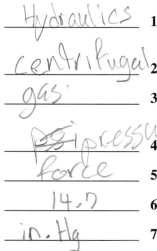

___Hydraulics___ **1.** ___ is the branch of science that deals with the practical application of water or other liquids at rest or in motion.

___Centrifugal___ **2.** ___ force is the outward force produced by a rotating object.

___gas___ **3.** A(n) ___ is a fluid that has neither independent shape nor volume and tends to expand indefinitely.

___psi pressure___ **4.** ___ is the force per unit area.

___force___ **5.** ___ is the energy that produces movement.

___14.7___ **6.** The weight of the atmosphere at sea level is ___ psia.

___in. Hg___ **7.** A mercury barometer is commonly calibrated in ___.

_78.54%_ **8.** The area of a circle is ___% of the area of a square with the same measurement.

vector **9.** A(n) ___ is a quantity that has a magnitude and direction.

mech. advant. **10.** Mechanical ___ is the ratio of the output force of a device to the input force.

energy **11.** ___ is a measure of the ability to do work.

work **12.** ___ is the energy used when a force is exerted over a distance.

Hydrostatics **13.** ___ is the study of liquids at rest and the forces exerted on them or by them.

equillibrium **14.** ___ is the condition when all forces and torques are balanced by equal and opposite forces and torques.

barometer **15.** A mercury ___ is an instrument that measures atmospheric pressure using a column of mercury.

vacuum **16.** ___ is a pressure lower than atmospheric pressure.

velocity **17.** ___ is the distance a fluid travels in a specified time.

fulcrum **18.** A(n) ___ is a support on which a lever turns or pivots and is located somewhere between the effort force and the resistance force.

kenetic **19.** ___ energy is the energy of motion.

torque **20.** ___ is the twisting (rotational) force of a shaft.

Hydrodynamics **21.** ___ is the study of the forces exerted on a solid body by the motion or pressure of a fluid.

absolute pressure **22.** ___ pressure is pressure above a perfect vacuum.

running **23.** ___ torque is the energy that a motor develops to keep a load turning.

_550_ **24.** One horsepower equals ___ ft lb/sec.

flow **25.** Fluid ___ is the movement of fluid caused by a difference in pressure between two points.

static **26.** ___ lift is the height to which atmospheric pressure causes a column of fluid to rise above the supply to restore equilibrium.

gauge **27.** ___ pressure is pressure above atmospheric pressure that is used to express pressures inside a closed system.

_0_ **28.** A pressure gauge reads ___ psig at normal atmospheric pressure.

acceleration **29.** ___ is an increase in speed.

lift **30.** Total column is fluid head plus ___.

Identification

Fluid Pressure

T   ~~F~~   **1.** The pressure at A is twice the pressure at D.

T   F   **2.** The pressure at B is the same as the pressure at C.

T   ~~F~~   **3.** The pressure at E is greater than the pressure at D.

T   ~~F~~   **4.** The pressure at F is the same as the pressure at D.

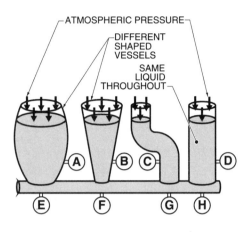

Lift

static   **1.** ___ lift is shown at Tank A.

dynamic   **2.** ___ lift is shown at Tank B.

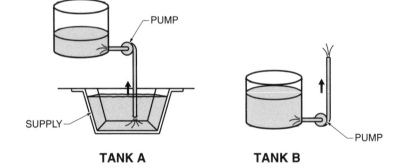

TANK A   **TANK B**

Fluid Flow

_~~8.170~~ 4.168_   **1.** The fluid velocity at A is ___ ft/sec. (Velocity is 4× greater in a pipe of ½ dia.)

_32.672_   **2.** The fluid velocity at B is ___ ft/sec. (Velocity is 4× greater in a pipe of ½ dia.)

~~T~~   F   **3.** The fluid velocity at C is ¼ the fluid velocity at A. (Velocity is 4× greater in a pipe of ½ dia.)

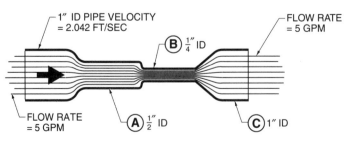

Horsepower

_2.62_

_2.18_

1. The horsepower required to lift Load A is ___ HP.

2. The horsepower required to lift Load B is ___ HP.

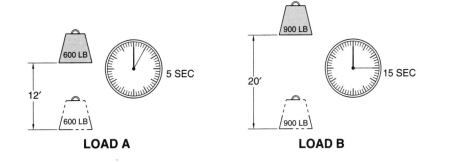

LOAD A

LOAD B

Hydrostatics

_D_

_A_

_B_

_C_

1. Heat energy

2. Static energy

3. Kinetic energy

4. External force

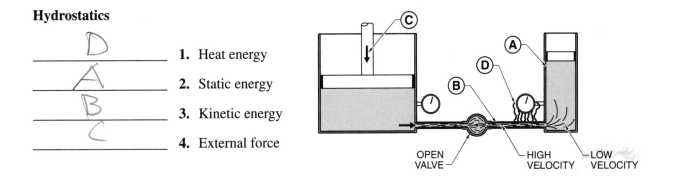

OPEN VALVE

HIGH VELOCITY

LOW VELOCITY

Mechanical Advantage

T   (F)   **1.** Gear B will turn in a clockwise direction.

T   (F)   **2.** Gear B will turn twice as fast as Gear A.

(T)   F   **3.** Gear B will turn with twice as much force as Gear A.

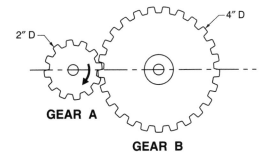

GEAR A

GEAR B

Problems

_____ 7,745 ____ **1.** Tank C has a capacity of ___ cu ft.

_____ 16 _____ **2.** Tank D has a capacity of ___ m³.

_____ 109.2psia ___ **3.** The absolute pressure in a system with a gauge pressure of 94.5 psig is ___ psia.

_____ 1.2272 in² __ **4.** The area of Piston A is ___ sq in.

_____ 815 psi _____ **5.** A pressure of ___ psi is required to move a 1000 lb force with Piston A.

_____ .75 gal _____ **6.** The amount of fluid required to fully extend a 3.5″ D cylinder with an 18″ stroke is ___ gal.

_____ 500 _____ **7.** A force of ___ lb is produced by a 4 sq in. piston operating at 125 psi.

_____ 3.26 _____ **8.** The velocity of a fluid having a flow rate of 4.5 gpm through a 1′ section of ¾″ D pipe is ___ ft/sec.

_____ 262.5 _____ **9.** The torque required to overcome the force at Winch A is ___ lb-in.

_____ 393.75 ____ **10.** If the distance in Problem 9 was increased to 5.25″, ___ lb-in would be required to overcome the force.

_____ 24 in² _____ **11.** The area of Surface A on Block A is ___ sq in.

_____ 72 in² _____ **12.** The area of Surface B on Block A is ___ sq ft.

_____ 144 in³ ____ **13.** The volume of Block A is ___ cu in.

_____ 4 _____ **14.** The velocity in Pipe A is ___ times greater than the velocity in Pipe B.

_____ 3.1416 ____ **15.** The area of Pipe A is ___ sq in.

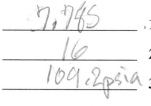

C — 3.5′, 1.5′ SQ

D — 2 m, 4 m, 2 m

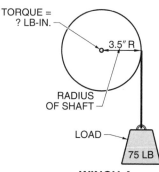

1.25″ D

PISTON A

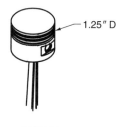

TORQUE = ? LB-IN.

3.5″ R

RADIUS OF SHAFT

LOAD

75 LB

WINCH A

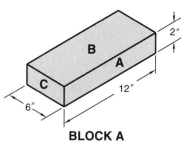

B, A, C
2″, 12″, 6″

BLOCK A

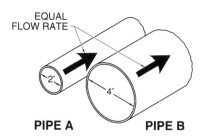

EQUAL FLOW RATE

2″, 4″

PIPE A   **PIPE B**

2857.48
16. The volume of Cylinder A is ___ cu in.

665.21
17. The volume of Cylinder B is ___ mm³.

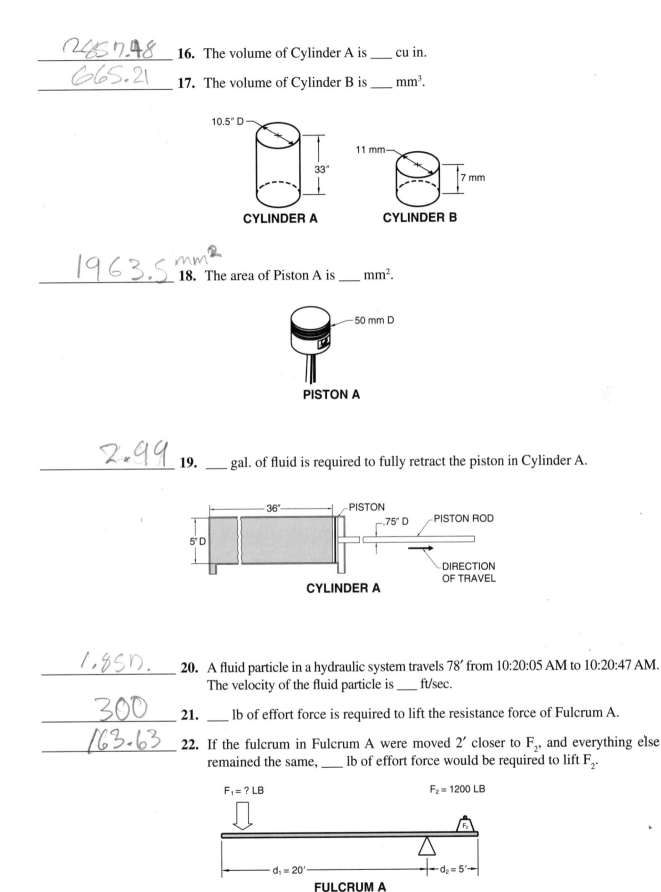

CYLINDER A   **CYLINDER B**

1963.5 mm²
18. The area of Piston A is ___ mm².

PISTON A

2.99
19. ___ gal. of fluid is required to fully retract the piston in Cylinder A.

CYLINDER A

1.85n.
20. A fluid particle in a hydraulic system travels 78′ from 10:20:05 AM to 10:20:47 AM. The velocity of the fluid particle is ___ ft/sec.

300
21. ___ lb of effort force is required to lift the resistance force of Fulcrum A.

163.63
22. If the fulcrum in Fulcrum A were moved 2′ closer to F_2, and everything else remained the same, ___ lb of effort force would be required to lift F_2.

FULCRUM A

_____1920_____ **23.** The torque required to overcome the force at Winch A is ___ lb-in.

_____720_____ **24.** If the load at Winch A was 120 lb, ___ lb-in would be required to overcome the force.

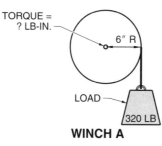

WINCH A

_____4.36_____ **25.** The horsepower required to lift the 3 t load is ___ HP.

_____.727_____ **26.** If the 3 t load took 1 min to be lifted the 4′ distance, the horsepower required would be ___ HP.

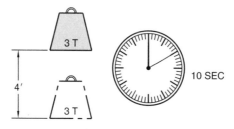

T   F   **27.** Load A requires more horsepower to be lifted than Load B.

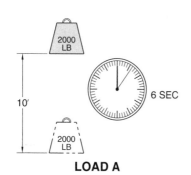

LOAD A

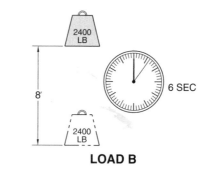

LOAD B

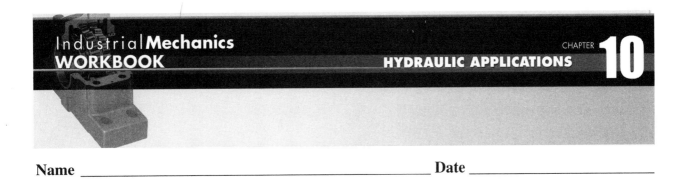

Name _____ **Date** _____

True-False

T F   **1.** Graphic symbols show flow paths, connections, and functions of components.

T F   **2.** Hydraulic fluids lubricate moving parts of a circuit.

T (F)   **3.** Strainer screens are rated in microns and filters are rated in mesh.

T F   **4.** A flared fitting is a fitting that is connected to tubing with an end that is spread outward.

(T) F   **5.** The higher the mesh number of a strainer, the smaller the opening.

T F   **6.** Tubing may be connected by welding or compression.

(T) (F)   **7.** Positive displacement is the moving of a fixed amount of a substance with each cycle of a hydraulic pump.

T F   **8.** A spur gear has straight teeth that are parallel to the shaft axis.

T F   **9.** A pressure-relief valve is a valve that sets a maximum operating pressure level for a circuit to protect the circuit from overpressure.

(T) F   **10.** Pipe is designated according to its nominal size and wall thickness.

(T) (F)   **11.** Tubes should always be assembled in a straight line.

(T) (F)   **12.** A ferrule is a metal sleeve used for joining one piece of tube to another.

T (F)   **13.** Vane pumps are the most widely used hydraulic pumps because of their simple design and ease of repair.

T (F)   **14.** Any hydraulic circuit must contain four essential elements.

(T) F   **15.** The volume of a vane pump is determined by how far the rotor and cam ring are offset.

Multiple Choice

_____ *C* _____ **1.** ___ is the combining of oxygen with oil, which breaks down the basic oil composition.
   A. Foaming
   B. Pitting
   C. Oxidation
   D. Cavitation

_____ *C* _____ **2.** A ___ filter is positioned in a hydraulic circuit just before the reservoir.
   A. suction
   B. pressure
   C. return-line
   D. none of the above

_____ *B* _____ **3.** A ___ is a device that transfers heat through a conducting wall from one fluid to another.
   A. fin cooler
   B. heat exchanger
   C. both A and B
   D. none of the above

_____ *C* _____ **4.** A ___ diagram is the layout, plan, or sketch of a hydraulic circuit and is designed to explain, demonstrate, or clarify the relationship between or functions of hydraulic components.
   A. pictorial
   B. cutaway
   C. hydraulic
   D. graphic

_____ *A* _____ **5.** Without a ___, dismantling of equipment can be required to determine the function of components within a circuit.
   A. graphic diagram
   B. piston pump
   C. cutaway diagram
   D. cam ring

_____ *C* _____ **6.** Hydraulic fluids are used to create ___ because they can be applied instantly throughout a system, allow for control at different locations, increase or decrease force, and change direction.
   A. resistance
   B. power
   C. force
   D. none of the above

_____ *B* _____ **7.** A(n) ___ is a substance that causes harm or damage to that with which it comes in contact.
   A. additive
   B. contaminant
   C. lubricant
   D. lichen

_____C_____ 8. ___ can be installed inside a reservoir at the fluid inlet of the system and placed in-line between the reservoir and the pump or installed on the exterior of a reservoir.
   A. Strainer screens
   B. Filters
   C. Suction strainers
   D. Pressure filters

___A___ B ___ 9. Maximum drop value for filters is typically ___ psi.
   A. 30
   B. 45
   C. 60
   D. 75

___B___ D ___ 10. Controlling pump ___ consumes the least horsepower while generating the least heat.
   A. input
   B. friction
   C. lubrication
   D. output

_____B_____ 11. ___ is caused by low inlet pressure and is a change in size of the air molecules normally found in hydraulic fluids.
   A. Pseudocavitation
   B. Cavitation
   C. Pump discharge
   D. all of the above

_____A_____ 12. A ___-damaged seal exhibits a hard and brittle material with cracks and a broken or chipped body or lip parts.
   A. heat
   B. chemicals
   C. contamination
   D. condensation

_____D_____ 13. Other work-habit causes of contamination or damage to seals include ___.
   A. improper handling of a seal before and during installation
   B. installation of the wrong seal
   C. installing a seal backwards
   D. all of the above

___A___ C ___ 14. ___ point is the temperature at which oil ignites by itself.
   A. Flash
   B. Fire
   C. Auto-ignition
   D. none of the above

_____C_____ 15. A Bourdon tube is ___.
   A. oval or elliptical in cross-sectional area
   B. bent in a C-shape
   C. both A and B
   D. none of the above

___D C___ 16. ___ is the capability of a material to regain its original shape after being bent, stretched, or compressed.
   A. Plasticity
   B. Revertance
   C. Resilience
   D. none of the above

___D___ 17. ___ are used in graphic diagrams to indicate an adjustable or variable component or to show shaft rotation on the near side of the shaft.
   A. Dashed lines
   B. Solid lines
   C. Dotted lines
   D. Arrows

___C___ 18. A ___ is a device containing a porous substance through which a fluid can pass but particulate matter cannot.
   A. funnel
   B. strainer
   C. filter
   D. mask

___B___ 19. A(n) ___ pump is a vane pump that has one set of internal ports and produces a pumping action in the chambers on one side of the rotor and shaft.
   A. balanced-vane
   B. unbalanced-vane
   C. pressure-compensated vane
   D. pressure-uncompensated vane

___A___ 20. A(n) ___ piston pump is a piston pump in which the angle of the swash plate can be varied.
   A. variable-displacement
   B. bent-axis
   C. axial
   D. radial

Completion

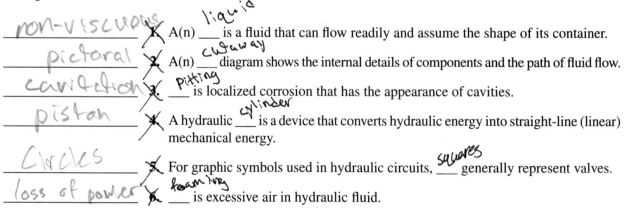

___non-viscuous___ ___liquid___ 1. A(n) ___ is a fluid that can flow readily and assume the shape of its container.

___pictoral___ ___cutaway___ 2. A(n) ___ diagram shows the internal details of components and the path of fluid flow.

___cavitation___ ___pitting___ 3. ___ is localized corrosion that has the appearance of cavities.

___piston___ ___cylinder___ 4. A hydraulic ___ is a device that converts hydraulic energy into straight-line (linear) mechanical energy.

___circles___ ___squares___ 5. For graphic symbols used in hydraulic circuits, ___ generally represent valves.

___loss of power___ ___foaming___ 6. ___ is excessive air in hydraulic fluid.

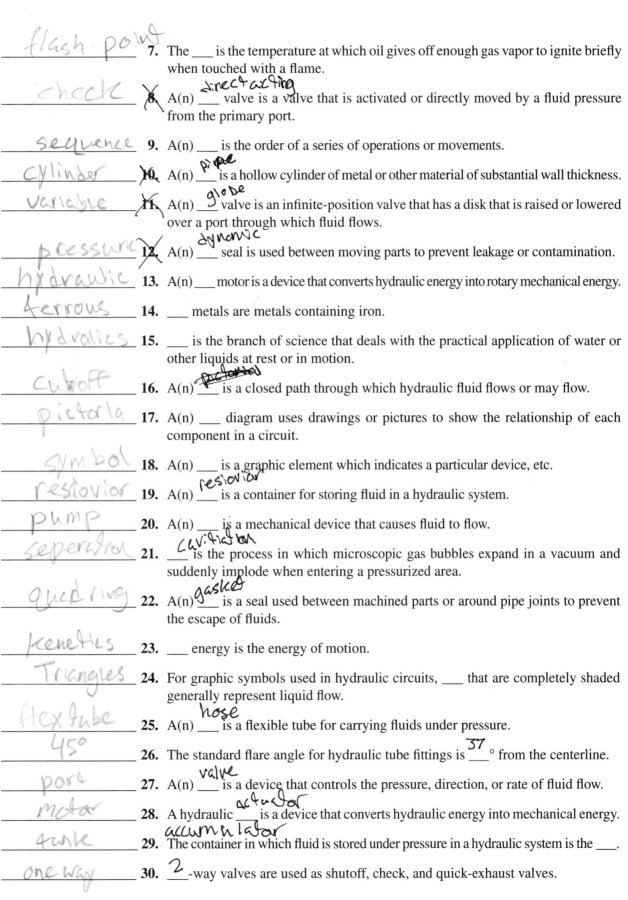

flash point **7.** The ___ is the temperature at which oil gives off enough gas vapor to ignite briefly when touched with a flame.

check ~~direct acting~~ **8.** A(n) ___ valve is a valve that is activated or directly moved by a fluid pressure from the primary port.

sequence **9.** A(n) ___ is the order of a series of operations or movements.

cylinder ~~pipe~~ **10.** A(n) ___ is a hollow cylinder of metal or other material of substantial wall thickness.

variable ~~globe~~ **11.** A(n) ___ valve is an infinite-position valve that has a disk that is raised or lowered over a port through which fluid flows.

pressure ~~dynamic~~ **12.** A(n) ___ seal is used between moving parts to prevent leakage or contamination.

hydraulic **13.** A(n) ___ motor is a device that converts hydraulic energy into rotary mechanical energy.

ferrous **14.** ___ metals are metals containing iron.

hydraulics **15.** ___ is the branch of science that deals with the practical application of water or other liquids at rest or in motion.

cutoff ~~pictorial~~ **16.** A(n) ___ is a closed path through which hydraulic fluid flows or may flow.

pictorla **17.** A(n) ___ diagram uses drawings or pictures to show the relationship of each component in a circuit.

symbol **18.** A(n) ___ is a graphic element which indicates a particular device, etc.

resiovior ~~resiovior~~ **19.** A(n) ___ is a container for storing fluid in a hydraulic system.

pump **20.** A(n) ___ is a mechanical device that causes fluid to flow.

seperatrol ~~cavitation~~ **21.** ___ is the process in which microscopic gas bubbles expand in a vacuum and suddenly implode when entering a pressurized area.

quad ring ~~gasket~~ **22.** A(n) ___ is a seal used between machined parts or around pipe joints to prevent the escape of fluids.

kenetics **23.** ___ energy is the energy of motion.

Triangles **24.** For graphic symbols used in hydraulic circuits, ___ that are completely shaded generally represent liquid flow.

flex tube ~~hose~~ **25.** A(n) ___ is a flexible tube for carrying fluids under pressure.

45° **26.** The standard flare angle for hydraulic tube fittings is ~~37~~ ° from the centerline.

port ~~valve~~ **27.** A(n) ___ is a device that controls the pressure, direction, or rate of fluid flow.

motor ~~actuator~~ **28.** A hydraulic ___ is a device that converts hydraulic energy into mechanical energy.

tank ~~accumulator~~ **29.** The container in which fluid is stored under pressure in a hydraulic system is the ___.

one way **30.** ~~2~~-way valves are used as shutoff, check, and quick-exhaust valves.

Identification

Diagram Color Coding

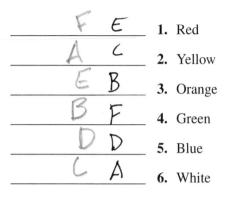

F E	**1.** Red
A C	**2.** Yellow
E B	**3.** Orange
B F	**4.** Green
D D	**5.** Blue
C A	**6.** White

A. inactive fluid

B. intermediate presssure that is lower than system operating pressure

C. controlled flow by a metering device or lowest working pressure

D. exhaust or return flow to the reservoir

E. fluid flowing at system operating pressure or highest working pressure

F. intake flow to pump or drain line flow

Graphic Symbols — Lines

A ——	**1.** Main line
B ∙∙∙ C	**2.** Pilot line

C ---- B	**3.** Drain line
D —∙—∙	**4.** Enclosure line

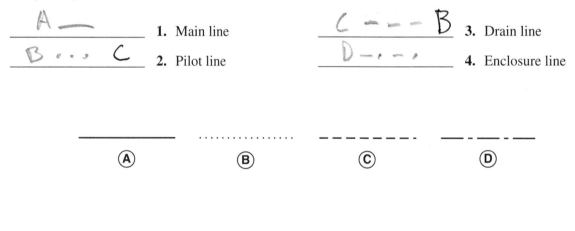

(A) (B) (C) (D)

Linear Equivalents

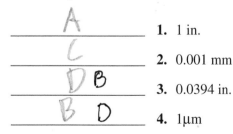

A	**1.** 1 in.
C	**2.** 0.001 mm
D B	**3.** 0.0394 in.
B D	**4.** 1μm

(A)	25.4 mm	25,400 μm
1 mm	(B)	1000 μm
1μm	25,400 of an in.	(C)
(D)	3.94 x 10⁻⁵ in.	0.000039 in.

Graphic Symbols—Squares or Rectangles

<u>D</u> **1.** Pressure switch

<u>A B</u> **2.** Single-acting cylinder

<u>C</u> **3.** Double-acting cylinder

<u>E A</u> **4.** Directional valve

<u>B E</u> **5.** Pressure-relief valve

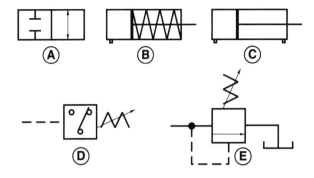

Gears

<u>A</u> **1.** Herringbone

<u>C</u> **2.** Helical

<u>B</u> **3.** Spur

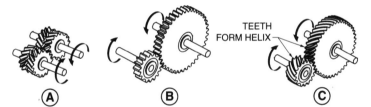

Pressure Gauge

<u>G I</u> **1.** Scale

<u>A F</u> **2.** Pivot

<u>H B</u> **3.** Spring

<u>I H</u> **4.** Pointer

<u>B G</u> **5.** Siphon connection

<u>J J</u> **6.** Pointer gear

<u>E A</u> **7.** Bourdon tube

<u>F L</u> **8.** Gear linkage

<u>C D</u> **9.** Linkage arm

<u>D E</u> **10.** Case

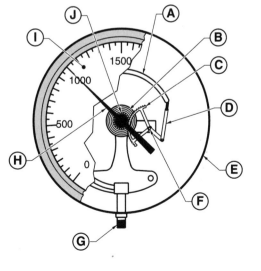

Check Valves

_____B_____ **1.** Poppet

_____A_____ **2.** Ball

_____C_____ **3.** Pilot-operated

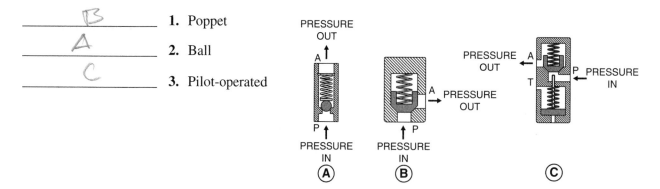

Graphic Symbols — Circles

__C__ B **1.** Pump

__B__ C **2.** Motor

__E__ A **3.** Pressure gauge

__A__ D **4.** Flow meter

__D__ E **5.** Check valve

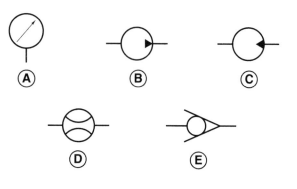

Graphic Symbols — Triangles

__C__ **1.** Motor

__A__ B **2.** Air compressor

__D__ D **3.** Bidirectional motor

__B__ A **4.** Direction of flow

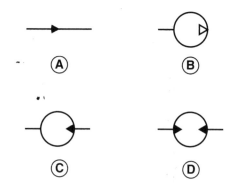

Flow Control Valves

_____ A 1. Restrictive check valve

_____ B C 2. Globe

_____ D B 3. Gate

_____ C D 4. Needle

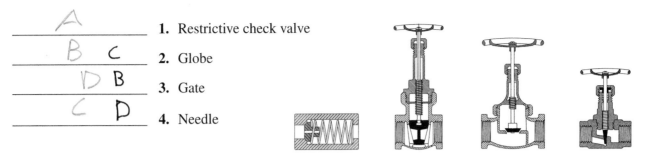

Filters

B 1. Pressure **B**

A 2. Suction **A**

B 3. Return-line **C**

Single Actuators

_____ D D 1. Manual

_____ A H 2. Pushbutton

_____ J J 3. Lever

_____ E I 4. Foot pedal

_____ C C 5. Solenoid

_____ H G 6. Mechanical

_____ B B 7. Detent

_____ I F 8. Air pilot

_____ F A 9. Spring

_____ G E 10. Oil pilot

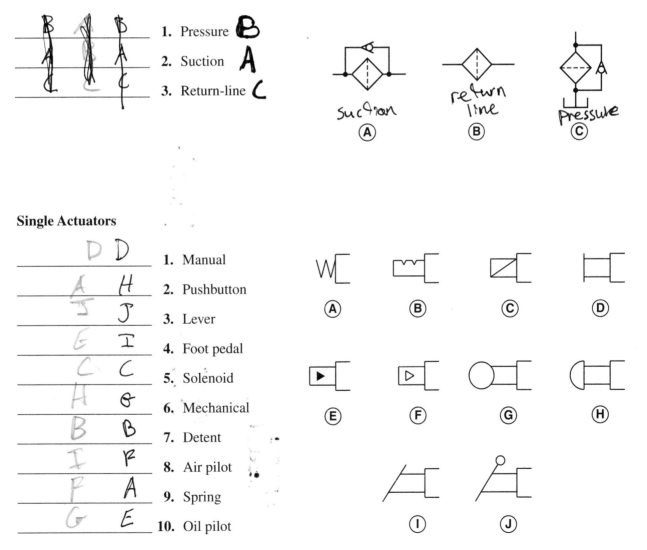

Problems

_____ **1.** The minimum bending radius of Tubing A is ~~3~~ 2″ R

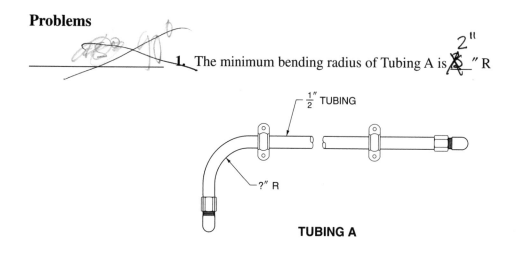

½″ TUBING

?″ R

TUBING A

2. Add a single-acting spring-return cylinder to Circuit A.

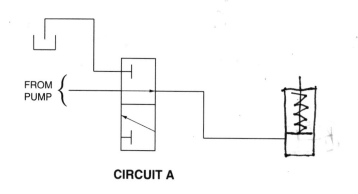

FROM
PUMP {

CIRCUIT A

3. Add a manually-actuated, spring-return, 3-way, two-position valve to control the cylinder in Circuit B.

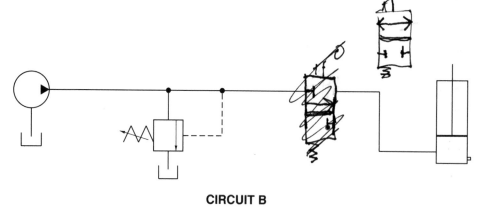

CIRCUIT B

4. The minimum bending radius of Hose A is __3__ " R.

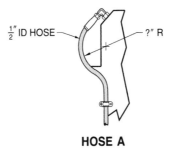

½" ID HOSE — ?" R

HOSE A

5. Add a pressure-relief valve to Circuit A.

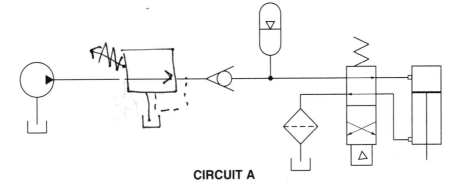

CIRCUIT A

6. Add a solenoid-actuated, spring-return, 4-way, two-position directional control valve to control the fluid flow in Circuit B.

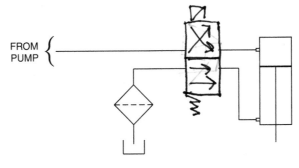

FROM PUMP {

CIRCUIT B

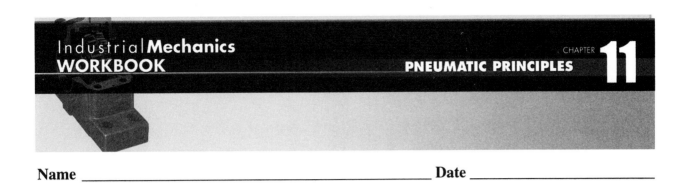

Name _____ Date _____

True-False

(T) F **1.** Gas can expand to fill the volume and shape of its container.

(T) F **2.** Gas molecules can be pushed closer together, allowing gas to be compressed.

T (F) **3.** The pressure in a container varies as the size or shape of the container varies.

T (F) **4.** In compression, air temperature decreases as a piston extends and the air molecules are forced closer together.

(T) F **5.** In an air compressor, multistage compression is required when the ratio of compression is greater than 6.

(T) F **6.** The amount of moisture air is capable of holding is greatly affected by the temperature of the air.

T (~~F~~) **7.** Guy-Lussac's law is used to determine pressure based on an increase in temperature.

T (F) **8.** An intercooler is a heat exchanger used for cooling the discharge from a compressor.

(T) F **9.** At standard pressure and temperature, the weight of 1 cu ft of air equals 0.076 lb.

T (F) **10.** A coalescing filter is a device that removes submicron solids and vapors of oil or water by breaking large droplets into very small droplets.

Multiple Choice

_____C_____ **1.** The temperature in °R is always ___° greater than the temperature in °F.
   A. 32
   B. 212
   (C.) 460
   D. 492

_____C_____ **2.** Free air is air at ___.
   (A.) atmospheric pressure
   B. ambient temperature
   (C.) both A and B
   D. none of the above

79

_____C_____ **3.** Atoms combine to form ___.
   A. protons
   B. particles
   (C) molecules
   D. none of the above

_____D_____ **4.** The pressure exerted on Earth's surface varies with ___.
   A. altitude
   B. temperature
   C. humidity
   (D) all of the above

_____A_____ **5.** ___ law states that the volume of a given quantity of gas varies inversely with the pressure as long as the temperature remains constant.
   (A) Boyle's
   B. Charles'
   C. Gay-Lussac's
   D. Pascal's

Completion

pneumatics **1.** ___ is the branch of science that deals with the transmission of energy using a gas.

atom **2.** A(n) ___ is the smallest building block of matter than cannot be divided into smaller units without changing its basic character.

psi pressure **3.** ___ is the force per unit area.

_14.7_ **4.** Atmospheric pressure at sea level is equal to about ___ psia.

volume **5.** ___ is the three-dimensional size of an object measured in cubic units.

~~positive~~ absolute **6.** ___ pressure is pressure above a perfect vacuum.

vacuum **7.** A(n) ___ is any pressure lower than atmospheric pressure.

zero **8.** Absolute ___ is the temperature at which substances possess no heat.

psig **9.** ___ pressure is the pressure above atmospheric pressure that is used to express pressures inside a closed system.

reciprocating **10.** A(n) ___ compressor is a device that compresses gas by means of a piston that moves back and forth in a cylinder.

*relative _Humidity_ **11.** ___ is the amount of moisture in the air.

particulate **12.** A(n) ___ is a fine solid particle that remains individually dispersed in a gas.

condensation **13.** ___ is the change in state from a gas or vapor to a liquid.

instrumentation **14.** ___ is the area of industry that deals with the measurement, evaluation, and control of process variables.

saturated **15.** ___ air is air that holds as much moisture as it is capable of holding.

Identification

States of Matter

_____ _A_ **1.** Solid

_____ _B_ **2.** Liquid

_____ _C_ **3.** Gas

Gas Laws

_____ _C_ **1.** Boyle's law

_____ _B_ **2.** Charles' law

_____ _A_ **3.** Gay-Lussac's law

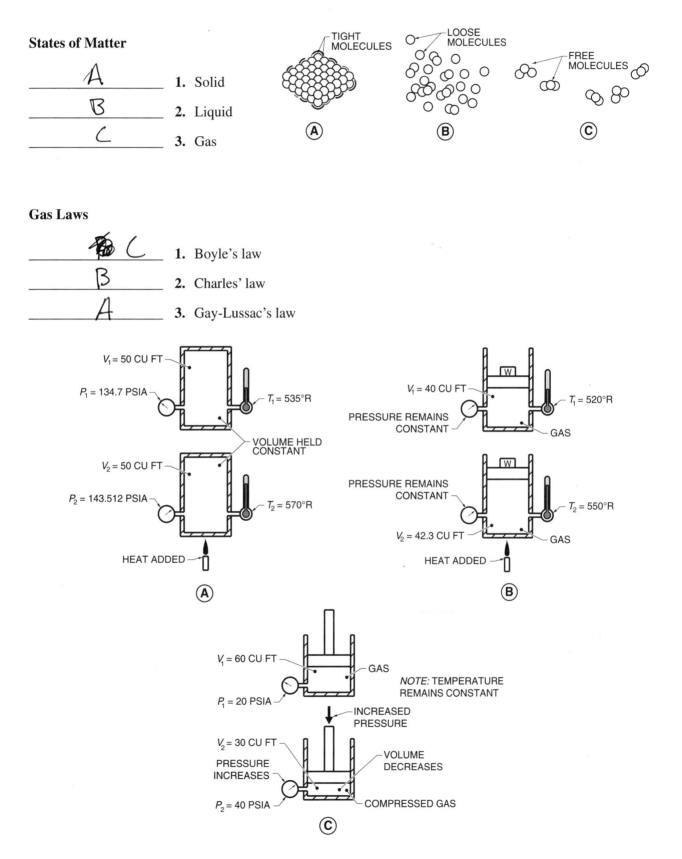

Desiccant Dryers

_____ B _____   **1.** Check valves

_____ D _____   **2.** Desiccant material

_____ ~~E~~ E _____   **3.** Reactivating dryer

_____ A _____   **4.** Moist air inlet

_____ H _____   **5.** Moist air outlet

_____ F _____   **6.** Dryer operating

_____ C _____   **7.** Purge valve

_____ ~~G~~ G _____   **8.** Dry air outlet

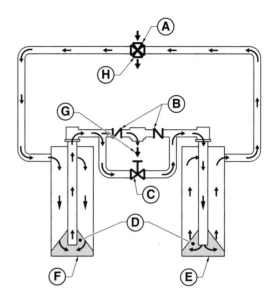

Fahrenheit/Rankine Temperatures

_____ E _____   **1.** −460

_____ F _____   **2.** 0

_____ C _____   **3.** 32

_____ A _____   **4.** 212

_____ D _____   **5.** 492

_____ B _____   **6.** 672

	°F	°R
WATER BOILS	Ⓐ	Ⓑ
WATER FREEZES	Ⓒ	Ⓓ
ABSOLUTE ZERO	Ⓔ	Ⓕ

Problems

_____ 66.84 _____   **1.** Tank A has a volume of ___ cu ft.

_____ 8975.31 _____   **2.** Tank B has a capacity of ___ gal.

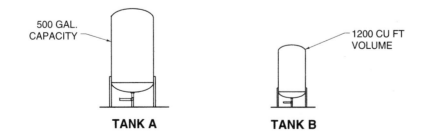

500 GAL. CAPACITY

TANK A

1200 CU FT VOLUME

TANK B

_____**542**_____

_____~~150~~ 125.769_____

_____~~99.24~~ **134.4**_____

_____**135**_____

_____~~1.40~~ 24.81_____

_____**106.6**_____

145.867

3. The temperature on the Fahrenheit scale equals ___°R.

4. The final volume of a gas that occupies 120 cu ft at 60°F is ___ cu ft at 85°F.

5. The final pressure in a 100 cu ft tank holding a gas at 90 psig at 75°F is ___ psig when the temperature is increased to 112°F.

6. The final volume of 90 cu ft of air at 45 psia is ___ cu ft when expanded to 30 psia.

7. The ratio of compression is ___ in a compressor with an inlet pressure of 1.25 psi vacuum and a discharge pressure of 50 psig.

8. The final pressure at Tank C is ___ psia.

—82°

°F

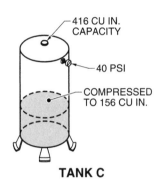

416 CU IN.
CAPACITY

40 PSI

COMPRESSED
TO 156 CU IN.

TANK C

26.178

_____~~46.94~~_____

_____**.6984**_____

_____**1.336**_____

9. Cylinder A has a capacity of ___ gal.

10. Fuel Can A has a volume of ___ cu ft.

11. Tub A has a volume of ___ cu ft.

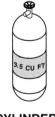

3.5 CU FT

CYLINDER A

5 GAL.

FUEL CAN A

10 GAL.

TUB A

_____42.7_____ **12.** The absolute pressure within Tire A is ___ psia.

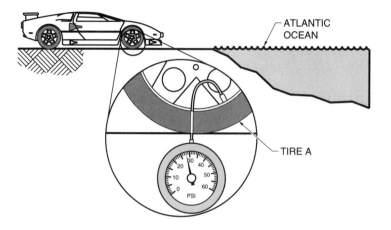

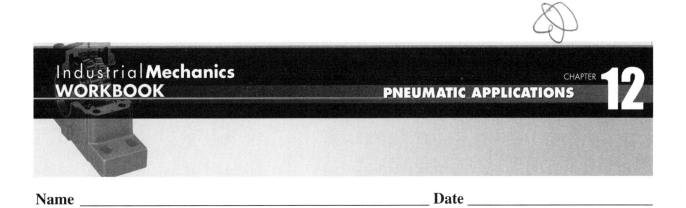
Name _____ Date _____

True-False

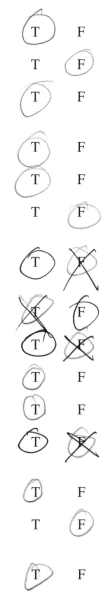

(T) F   **1.** A symbol is a graphic element which indicates a particular device.

T **(F)**   **2.** Thread-lubricating material should be placed in the female fitting only.

(T) F   **3.** The symbols for most of the components used in a pneumatic circuit are similar to those used in hydraulic circuits.

(T) F   **4.** Logic is the science of correct reasoning.

(T) F   **5.** An O-ring may be used as a static or a dynamic seal.

T **(F)**   **6.** An air motor is an air-driven device that converts rotary mechanical energy into fluid energy.

(T) ~~F~~   **7.** A truth table lists the output condition of a logic element or combination of logic elements for every possible input condition.

~~T~~ **(F)**   **8.** Electric motors are less efficient than air motors.

(T) ~~F~~   **9.** Air motors are lighter than direct replacement electric motors.

(T) F   **10.** The most popular air motor is the vane air motor.

(T) F   **11.** Pneumatic circuits are generally cleaner than hydraulic circuits.

(T) ~~F~~   **12.** An intensifier is a device that converts low-pressure fluid power into high-pressure fluid power.

(T) F   **13.** All pneumatic circuits are designed based on how energy is used to perform work.

T **(F)**   **14.** An AND logic element is a logic element that provides a logic level 1 if one or more inputs are at logic level 1.

(T) F   **15.** The maximum pressure drop in a system should be less than 10% above the system operating pressure.

Multiple Choice

_____ **D** **1.** A(n) ___ is the screw helix of a rotor.
A. tongue
B. ear
C. leaf
D. lobe

_____ **B** **2.** Draining liquid is generally accomplished by installing the main header at a downward pitch of ___.
A. 1″ for every 1′
B. 1″ for every 10′
C. 10″ for every 10′
D. none of the above

_____ **C** **3.** A binary system has ___ value(s).
A. no
B. one
C. two
D. any number of

_____ **D** **4.** A(n) ___ displacement compressor compresses a fixed quantity of air with each cycle.
A. manual or automatic
B. electric or gasoline
C. vertical or horizontal tank
D. none of the above

_____ **A** **5.** A(n) ___ is a device that senses a high- or low-pressure condition and relays an electrical signal to turn the compressor motor ON or OFF.
A. pressure switch
B. unloading valve
C. safety relief valve
D. none of the above

_____ **B** **6.** A(n) ___ is a device that senses a high-pressure condition and removes the compression energy.
A. pressure switch
B. unloading valve
C. safety relief valve
D. none of the above

_____ **C** **7.** A(n) ___ is a device that prevents excessive pressure from building up by venting air to the atmosphere.
A. pressure switch
B. unloading valve
C. safety relief valve
D. none of the above

_____ D **8.** The prime mover in a helical screw compressor normally rotates the rotors at speeds between 3000 rpm and ___ rpm.
  A. 6000
  B. 8000
  C. 10,000
  D. 12,000

_____ C **9.** A ¼″ hole in a pneumatic system that has an initial pressure of 80 psig loses about ___ scfm.
  A. 50.0
  B. 68.0
  C. 85.5
  D. 104

_____ A **10.** A single-stage vane compressor normally has operating pressures between ___ psi and ___ psi.
  A. 0, 50
  B. 0, 100
  C. 0, 125
  D. 50, 125

_____ D **11.** A two-stage vane compressor normally has operating pressures between ___ psi and ___ psi.
  A. 0, 50
  B. 0, 100
  C. 50, 100
  D. 50, 125

_____ B **12.** An example of a(n) ___ application is a hard tire pump used to pump air into bicycle tires.
  A. actuator
  B. check valve
  C. directional control valve
  D. gate valve

_____ C **13.** The outlet pressure produced by a 36″ D operating piston and a 24″ D ram operating at an inlet pressure of 350 psi is ___ psi.
  A. 155.55
  B. 225.00
  C. 525.00
  D. 787.50

_____ D **14.** Pressure loss in a pneumatic system is the result of the ___.
  A. resistance created within the system
  B. work load demands
  C. size and length of pipe
  D. all of the above

_____C_____ **15.** A(n) ___ pressure regulator uses a metallic or nylon-reinforced rubber diaphragm to sense a pressure differential between a regulating spring and a disc spring.

    A. one-way

    B. two-way

    C. diaphragm

    D. piston

Completion

____System____ **1.** A pneumatic ___ transmits and controls energy through the use of a pressurized gas within an enclosed circuit.

Air compressor **2.** A(n) ___ is a device that takes air from the atmosphere and compresses it to increase its pressure.

___reciprocate___ **3.** To ___ is to move forward and backward alternately.

___connecting___ **4.** A(n) ___ rod is the rod that connects the crankshaft to the piston.

___compensator___ **5.** A pressure ___ is a displacement control that alters displacement in response to pressure changes in a system.

_____one_____ **6.** A check valve allows flow in only ___ direction(s).

_____vane_____ **7.** A(n) ___ compressor is a positive-displacement compressor that has multiple vanes located in an offset rotor.

____header____ **8.** A main ___ is the main air supply line that runs between the receiver and the circuits in a pneumatic system.

____filter____ **9.** A(n) ___ is a device containing a porous substance through which a fluid can pass but particulate matter cannot.

_____10_____ **10.** Lubricators should be placed no more than ___' from the lubricated components.

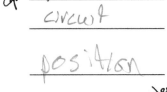 **11.** A pressure ___ is a value that restricts and/or blocks downstream air flow.

~~solenoid~~ **12.** A(n) ___ is a device that converts electrical energy into a linear, mechanical force.

____circuit____ **13.** A pneumatic ___ is a combination of air-operated components that are connected to perform work.

___position___ **14.** A(n) ___ is the specific location of a spool within a valve which determines the direction of fluid flow through the valve.

~~piston~~ cylinder **15.** An air ___ is a device that converts compressed air energy into linear mechanical energy.

____static____ **16.** A(n) ___ seal is a seal used as a gasket to seal nonmoving parts.

___dynamic___ **17.** A(n) ___ seal is a seal used between moving parts that prevents leakage or contamination.

__flow control__ **18.** ___ valves are normally used for metering air flow to control motor speed, cylinder piston speed, or valve spool shifting speed (for timing).

Identification

Graphic Diagram—Pneumatic System

_____ F _____ **1.** Electric motor

_____ G _____ **2.** Filter

_____ ~~D~~ I _____ **3.** Aftercooler

_____ D _____ **4.** Separator

_____ A _____ **5.** Pressure switch

_____ ~~A~~ E _____ **6.** Compressor

_____ ~~~~ C _____ **7.** Receiver

_____ H _____ **8.** Safety relief valve

_____ ~~~~ B _____ **9.** Manual shut-off valve

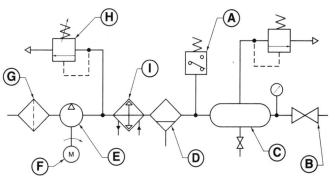

Graphic Diagram—Pneumatic Circuit

_____ D _____ **1.** Flow from compressor

_____ A _____ **2.** Actuator

_____ C _____ **3.** Regulator

_____ F _____ **4.** Lubricator

_____ E _____ **5.** Filter

_____ B _____ **6.** Directional control valve

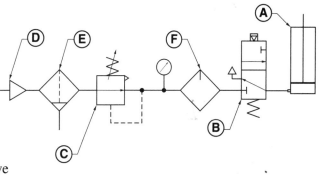

Safety Relief Valves

_____ B _____ **1.** Spring

_____ D _____ **2.** System pressure

_____ ~~~~ G _____ **3.** Valve vent port

_____ C _____ **4.** Seat

_____ E _____ **5.** Poppet

_____ A _____ **6.** Pull ring

_____ ~~~~ F _____ **7.** Vent to atmosphere

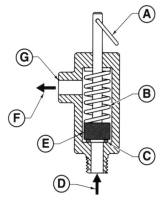

Pneumatic System Symbols

_____ *C*   **1.** Pipe slope in direction of flow

_____ *E*   **2.** Liquid separator with automatic drain

_____ *D*   **3.** Filter with manual drain

_____ *F*   **4.** Lubricator with manual drain

_____ *A*   **5.** Gate valve

_____ *B*   **6.** Quick disconnect

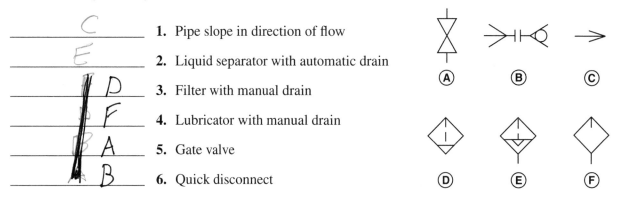

Problems

~~*1333.7*~~ *1334.84*

Pg. 339

1. The outlet pressure produced by the intensifier is ___ psi.

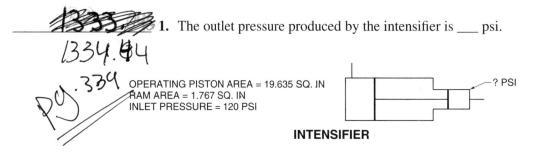

OPERATING PISTON AREA = 19.635 SQ. IN
RAM AREA = 1.767 SQ. IN
INLET PRESSURE = 120 PSI

? PSI

INTENSIFIER

3.4 ~~...~~   **2.** The main header should drop ___″ from the receiver to the moisture drop pipe.

~~...~~ *.061*   **3.** The pressure drop in a pneumatic system with 119′ of 2″ Schedule 40 pipe, one 2″ globe valve, two 2″ 45° elbows, and one 25 μ filter that has a working pressure of 110 psi and an airflow rate of 70 scfm is ___ psi.

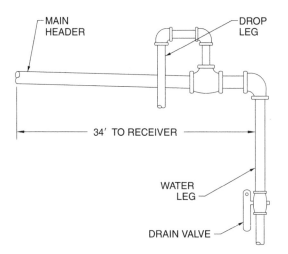

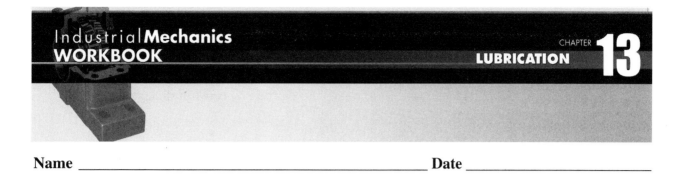

Name _____ Date _____

True-False

T	F	**1.**	Walking requires friction between the feet and floor in order to move.
T	F	**2.**	Lubrication generally involves coating surfaces with a material that has a higher coefficient of friction than the original surfaces.
T	F	**3.**	Friction occurs when an object in contact with another object tries to move.
T	F	**4.**	Animal and vegetable oils are used mostly in the food industry.
T	F	**5.**	Petroleum is composed of 12% carbon and 85% hydrogen, with a small amount of other elements.
T	F	**6.**	Animal and vegetable oils contain fatty acids.
T	F	**7.**	The grease used in a centralized system should be one grade softer than is otherwise required.
T	F	**8.**	Sealed bearings should be relubricated on a regularly-scheduled basis.
T	F	**9.**	Shear stress is stress in which the material on one side of a surface pushes on the material on the other side of the surface with a force perpendicular to the surface.
T	F	**10.**	Synthetic lubricants are generally higher priced than petroleum lubricants.
T	F	**11.**	Lubrication contamination is the main cause of mechanical system failure.
T	F	**12.**	Oil that is contaminated with water has a clear appearance.
T	F	**13.**	Petroleum is formed by an evolutionary process that takes many millions of years.
T	F	**14.**	Greater force is required to move a body from a static condition than is required to keep it in a kinetic condition.
T	F	**15.**	The flow rate is the most important property of a lubricant.
T	F	**16.**	Under basic conditions, as the temperature of oils increases, their viscosity also increases.

91

T F   **17.** Lubricating oil is given an SAE viscosity rating based on its ability to flow at a specific temperature.

T F   **18.** A 10 weight oil is thicker than a 40 weight oil.

T F   **19.** Solid lubricants such as graphite shear easily between sliding surfaces.

T F   **20.** All greases exhibit a dropping point.

T F   **21.** Water that mixes with lubricants increases the effectiveness of the lubricant.

T F   **22.** As temperatures increase, greases become softer.

T F   **23.** Graphite has high shearing forces.

T F   **24.** Gas lubricants are commonly used in low-friction, high-speed, high-technology applications.

T F   **25.** Overgreasing leads to overheating, aerating, and churning of the grease, resulting in early bearing failure.

Multiple Choice

_____ **1.** Lubricants are used to ___.
    A. reduce friction
    B. prevent wear
    C. prevent corrosion
    D. all of the above

_____ **2.** Liquid lubricants include ___.
    A. animal/vegetable oils
    B. petroleum fluids
    C. synthetic fluids
    D. all of the above

_____ **3.** During startup of a machine, oil ___.
    A. is cool
    B. does not flow easily
    C. A and B
    D. none of the above

_____ **4.** ___ action is the action by which the surface of a liquid is elevated on a material due to its relative molecular attraction.
    A. Submission
    B. Polymeric
    C. Capillary
    D. none of the above

_____ **5.** ___ lubrication is the condition of lubrication in which the friction between two surfaces in motion is determined by the properties of the surfaces and the properties of the lubricant other than viscosity.
    A. Area
    B. Material
    C. Surface
    D. none of the above

_____ **6.** A(n) ___ lubricant is a lubricant that uses pressurized air to separate two surfaces.
    A. chemical
    B. metal
    C. gas
    D. none of the above

_____ **7.** A ___ solid is a solid that is finely ground in order to be spread.
    A. disposed
    B. dispersed
    C. dispelled
    D. displaced

_____ **8.** A ___ is the result of a chemical reaction in which two or more small molecules combine to form larger molecules.
    A. polygon
    B. polymer
    C. either A or B
    D. none of the above

_____ **9.** A ___ system is a lubrication system that contains permanently installed plumbing, distribution valves, a reservoir, and a pump to provide lubrication.
    A. centralized
    B. wick
    C. drip
    D. submersion

_____ **10.** A grease is a ___ lubricant created by combining low-viscosity oils with thickeners, such as soap or other finely dispersed solids.
    A. gas
    B. liquid
    C. semisolid
    D. solid

Completion

_____ **1.** ___ is the process of maintaining a fluid film between solid surfaces to prevent their physical contact.

_____ **2.** The ___ of friction is the measure of frictional force between two surfaces in contact.

_____ 3. ___ is a chemical adsorption process in which weak chemical bonds are formed between liquid or gas molecules and solid surfaces.

_____ 4. ___ gases are gases that lack active properties.

_____ 5. Earth's plants release approximately ___ million tons of hydrocarbons into the air each year.

_____ 6. ___ is the measurement of the resistance of a fluid's molecules to move past each other.

_____ 7. Shear ___ is a liquid's ability to remain as a separator between solids in motion.

_____ 8. A(n) ___ is a device that vaporizes elements in the oil sample into light.

_____ 9. A petroleum fluid is a fluid consisting of ___.

_____ 10. Wear particle ___ is the study of wear particles present in lubricating oil.

_____ 11. Fluid lubricants must create a(n) ___ between material surfaces to prevent contact with each other.

_____ 12. Petroleum fluids make up approximately ___% of the total lubricants used.

_____ 13. Oil film thickness ___ with an increase in oil temperature.

_____ 14. The grease ___ is the maximum temperature a grease withstands before it softens enough to flow through a laboratory testing orifice.

_____ 15. The ___ the viscosity rating number, the thicker the oil.

Identification

Grease Thickeners

_____ 1. Aluminum soap   **A.** used for extreme temperatures

_____ 2. Calcium soap   **B.** added to resist being thrown off

_____ 3. Lithium soap   **C.** offers clarity

_____ 4. Clay   **D.** is water-resistant

_____ 5. Fiber   **E.** allows high-temperature use

Oil Application Systems

_____ **1.** Submersion–Splash

_____ **2.** Submersion–Chain

_____ **3.** Submersion–Ring

_____ **4.** Drip

_____ **5.** Wick

_____ **6.** Centralized

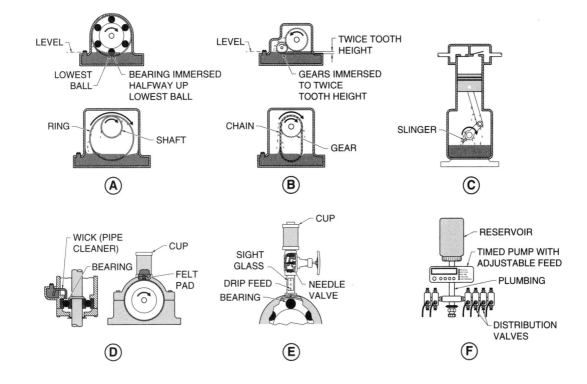

Lubricant Additives

_____ **1.** Oxidation inhibitors

_____ **2.** Rust inhibitors

_____ **3.** Fatty materials

_____ **4.** Powdered lead or graphite

_____ **5.** Viscosity index improvers

_____ **6.** Demulsifiers

A. prevent rust

B. improve film strength

C. prevent galling

D. separate out water

E. provide long bearing or gear life

F. ease machine movement in cold weather

Oil Groups/Application

_____ **1.** Group A

_____ **2.** Group B

_____ **3.** Group C

_____ **4.** Group D

_____ **5.** Group E

_____ **6.** Group F

A. machine tools

B. automotive

C. reciprocating engines

D. turbojet engines

E. gear trains and transmissions

F. marine propulsions and stationary power turbines

Petroleum

_____ **1.** Pilot oil well

_____ **2.** Crude oil pumped from well

_____ **3.** Soil

_____ **4.** Porous rock

_____ **5.** Nonporous rock

_____ **6.** Bedrock

_____ **7.** Crude oil

_____ **8.** Natural gas

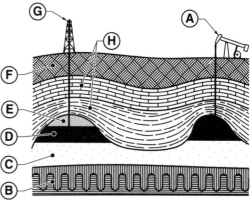

Motor Regreasing

_____ **1.** Wipe grease fitting, drain plug, and grease gun nozzle.

_____ **2.** Remove drain plug and clean.

_____ **3.** Add grease until grease is expelled from drain plug port.

_____ **4.** Run motor to expel excess grease.

_____ **5.** Clean and replace drain plug.

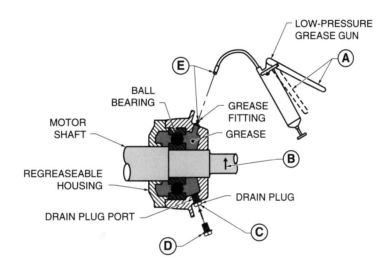

Grease Application Methods

_____ **1.** Grease cup

_____ **2.** Grease gun

_____ **3.** Centralized system

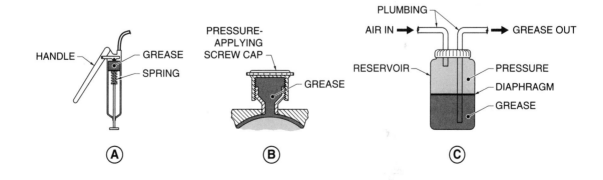

NLGI Grease Grades

T F   **1.** The higher the NLGI number, the stiffer the grease.

T F   **2.** The higher the NLGI number, the more penetration it has.

T F   **3.** Grade 1 is softer than Grade 00.

T F   **4.** Grade 000 has three times the penetration of Grade 0.

T F   **5.** Grades 0, 1, and 2 are the most widely used in industry.

T F   **6.** For maximum penetration, a higher NLGI grade of grease should be used.

_____ **7.** Grade 5 will penetrate approximately one-half as much as Grade ___.

_____ **8.** NLGI Grade ___ has a penetration range from 0.68″ to 0.80″.

NLGI GREASE GRADES		
NLGI Grade	**Penetration***	**Stiffness**
000	1.75 – 1.87	VERY SOFT
00	1.57 – 1.69	
0	1.32 – 2.30	
1	1.22 – 1.33	
2	1.04 – 1.16	
3	0.86 – 0.98	
4	0.68 – 0.80	
5	0.51 – 0.62	
6	0.33 – 0.45	VERY HARD

* in in.

Problems

T F   **1.** The coefficient of friction of Object B is 5.

_____ **2.** The coefficient of friction of Object A is ___.

_____ **3.** A 40 lb force is required to overcome the frictional force between a 75 lb object and the surface upon which it is resting. The coefficient of friction is ___.

OBJECT A

10 LB 30 LB

OBJECT B

8 LB 40 LB

Coefficients of Friction

T   F   **1.** Greater force is required to move a body from rest than is required to keep it in motion.

T   F   **2.** The static condition relating to coefficient of friction refers to the forces required to start a solid object in motion.

T   F   **3.** Gas lubricants can operate in temperatures from –400°F to over 3500°F.

T   F   **4.** The static coefficient of friction for unlubricated copper-to-copper surfaces is higher than that for unlubricated steel-to-steel surfaces.

_____   **5.** The coefficient of friction of a 500 lb object resting on a horizontal surface that requires 125 lb of force to move is ___.
    A. 0.03
    B. 0.25
    C. 0.40
    D. 4.0

_____   **6.** The coefficient of friction of a 3500 lb object resting on a horizontal surface that requires 225 lb of force to move is ___.
    A. 0.06
    B. 0.16
    C. 0.64
    D. 15.6

_____   **7.** The coefficient of friction of a 2200 lb object resting on a horizontal surface that requires 931 lb of force to move is ___.
    A. 0.42
    B. 0.84
    C. 0.95
    D. 1.1

_____   **8.** The coefficient of friction of a 51 lb object resting on a horizontal surface that requires 6 lb of force to move is ___.
    A. 0.01
    B. 0.12
    C. 0.85
    D. 8.5

_____   **9.** The coefficient of friction of a 23¼ lb object resting on a horizontal surface that requires 2.11 lb of force to move is ___.
    A. 0.09
    B. 0.11
    C. 0.92
    D. 11

_____ **10.** The coefficient of friction required to start the movement of a piece of copper resting on an unlubricated copper plate is ___.

_____ **11.** The coefficient of friction required to maintain the movement of a piece of copper on an unlubricated copper plate is ___.

_____ **12.** A steel object resting on an unlubricated piece of steel weighs 10 lb. A force of ___ lb is required to start it in motion.

COEFFICIENTS OF FRICTION				
Material	**Unlubricated**		**Lubricated***	
	Static	**Kinetic**	**Static**	**Kinetic**
Steel-to-Steel	0.8	00	0.16	0.02
Copper-to-Copper	1.5	0.3	0.08	0.02
Aluminum-to-Aluminum	1.3	—	0.3	—
Nylon-to-Nylon	0.3	0.1	—	—
Teflon-to-Teflon	0.04	0.03	—	—
Graphite-to-Graphite	0.1	0.06	—	—

*values are approximations and vary according to lubricant type

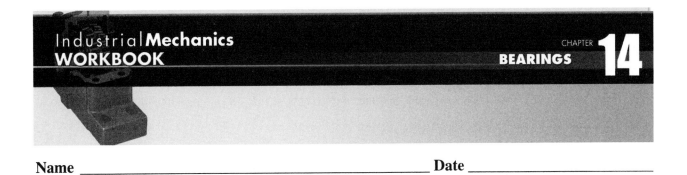

Name _____ Date _____

True-False

T   F   **1.** Doubling the load on a bearing increases its service life by 6 to 8 times.

T   F   **2.** A better finish on a bearing produces less friction.

T   F   **3.** Ball bearings are installed with one ring being a press fit and the other ring a push fit.

T   F   **4.** Needle bearings are generally press fit.

T   F   **5.** Plain bearings may support radial and axial loads.

T   F   **6.** Bearing installation is generally more difficult than bearing removal.

T   F   **7.** Bearings should never be struck with a hammer.

T   F   **8.** Solid or caked lubricant is a sign that bearings have overheated.

T   F   **9.** As the temperature of steel increases, it discolors, turning from silver to blue to black.

T   F   **10.** Prelubricated bearings may be heated for installation.

T   F   **11.** Never apply pressure on the outer ring if the inner ring is press fit and never apply pressure on the inner ring if the outer ring is press fit.

T   F   **12.** Roller-contact bearings include ball, roller, and needle bearings.

T   F   **13.** Needle bearings are designed primarily for relatively low radial loads.

T   F   **14.** Babbitt metals are the best metals for plain bearing loads.

T   F   **15.** False Brinell damage is bearing damage caused by forces passing from one ring to the other through the balls or rollers.

T   F   **16.** A machine should never be grounded by connecting a wire from the machine to a gas or oil pipe.

T   F   **17.** More bearings are destroyed, damaged, and abused during the installation stage than from malfunction during their life expectancy.

T F **18.** A roller bearing is an anti-friction bearing that permits free motion between a moving part and a fixed part by means of balls confined between inner and outer rings.

T F **19.** Porous bronze bearings become self-lubricating when impregnated with oil.

T F **20.** When installing bearings, they may be struck with a wooden mallet or wooden block.

Multiple Choice

_____ **1.** The ___ is the track on which the balls of a bearing move.
  A. cup
  B. cone
  C. race
  D. none of the above

_____ **2.** Under normal load conditions, ball bearings generally have ___″ interference per inch of shaft when the inner race is press fit.
  A. 0.00025
  B. 0.0025
  C. 0.025
  D. 0.25

_____ **3.** A(n) ___ bearing is a rolling-contact bearing in which the load is transmitted perpendicularly to the axis of shaft rotation.
  A. angular contact
  B. Conrad
  C. loading
  D. radial

_____ **4.** A(n) ___ slot is a groove or notch on the inside wall of each bearing ring to allow insertion of balls.
  A. angular
  B. ball
  C. loading
  D. ring

_____ **5.** Bearings that are designed for ___ loads must be installed in only one direction to prevent the load from separating the bearing components.
  A. compression
  B. low-weight
  C. tensile
  D. thrust

_____ **6.** Double-row bearings are also known as ___ bearings.
  A. ball
  B. duplex
  C. needle
  D. plain

_____ 7. Cylindrical roller bearings are used in high-speed, high-load applications and may contain as many as ___ rows of rollers.
  A. four
  B. six
  C. eight
  D. twelve

_____ 8. ___ bearings are suited for chemical or high-temperature applications and require no lubrication.
  A. Antimony
  B. Bronze
  C. Copper-lead
  D. Nylon and Teflon

_____ 9. ___ bearings are designed to operate in temperatures exceeding 700°F and withstand 300 psi of load force without a lubricant.
  A. Aluminum
  B. Carbon-graphite
  C. Lead
  D. Nylon and Teflon

_____ 10. ___ damage on ball bearings appears as marks on the shoulder or upper portion of the inner and outer races and will be anywhere from a slight discoloration to heavy galling.
  A. Misalignment
  B. Pitting
  C. Spalling
  D. Thrust

_____ 11. When mounting bearings through the use of controlled temperatures, temperatures over ___°F may reduce the hardness of bearing metals, resulting in early failure.
  A. 250
  B. 300
  C. 350
  D. 400

_____ 12. Bearings are classified as ___ or plain bearings.
  A. friction
  B. direct
  C. rolling-contact
  D. static

_____ 13. ___ corrosion is the rusty appearance that results when two metals in contact are vibrated, rubbing loose minute metal particles that become oxidized.
  A. Spalling
  B. Pitting
  C. Fluting
  D. none of the above

_____ **14.** Deviations of more than ___″ in precision class bearing assemblies can cause significant vibration.
     A. 0.0002
     B. 0.0005
     C. 0.002
     D. 0.005

_____ **15.** A ___ bearing is an anti-friction roller-type bearing with long rollers of small diameter.
     A. ball
     B. needle
     C. roller
     D. plain

Completion

_____ **1.** A(n) ___ is a machine part that supports another part, such as a shaft, which rotates or slides in or on it.

_____ **2.** ___ life is the maximum useful life of a bearing.

_____ **3.** A(n) ___ load is a load in which the applied force is parallel to the axis of rotation.

_____ **4.** ___ life is the length of service received from a bearing.

_____ **5.** A(n) ___ bearing is a bearing in which the shaft turns and is lubricated by a sleeve.

_____ **6.** ___ is the flaking away of metal pieces due to metal fatigue.

_____ **7.** The ___ of grease is the temperature at which the oil in grease separates from the thickener and runs out, leaving just the thickener.

_____ **8.** Bearing surfaces that are ___ appear as worn surfaces on one side or opposing sides of a bearing.

_____ **9.** ___ is a bonding, shearing, and tearing away of material from two contacting, sliding metals.

_____ **10.** ___ damage is bearing damage due to axial force.

_____ **11.** ___ is the elongated and rounded grooves or tracks left by the etching of each roller on the rings of an improperly grounded roller bearing during welding.

_____ **12.** Precision class bearings are generally marked with their high points of ___.

_____ **13.** ___ play is the total amount of axial movement of a shaft.

_____ **14.** A ___-contact bearing is a bearing composed of rolling elements between an inner and outer ring.

_____ **15.** A threaded cup ___ is a tapered bearing gap adjusting device that is used to adjust shaft endplay by controlling the amount of clearance between the bearings.

_____ **16.** A(n) ___ bore bearing is a bearing that uniformly increases or decreases from one face to the opposite face.

_____ **17.** A(n) ___ is the part of a shaft, such as an axle or spindle, that moves in a plain bearing.

_____ **18.** ___ is an initial pressure placed on a bearing when axial load forces are expected to be great enough to overcome preload force.

_____ **19.** Metal ___ is the fracturing of worked metal due to normal operating conditions or overload situations.

_____ **20.** A(n) ___ bearing is a single-row ball bearing without a loading slot that has deeper-than-normal races.

Identification

Bearing Failure

_____ **1.** Dark, discolored metals indicate ___.

_____ **2.** Rusting surfaces indicate ___.

_____ **3.** Split or fractured rings indicate ___.

A. improper fit or assembly

B. high temperatures

C. high moisture and/or improper lubrication

Angular Contact Bearing Use

_____ **1.** Face-to-face

_____ **2.** Back-to-back

_____ **3.** Separated face-to-face

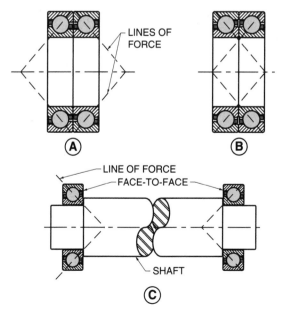

Bearing Loads

_____ **1.** Radial load

_____ **2.** Axial load

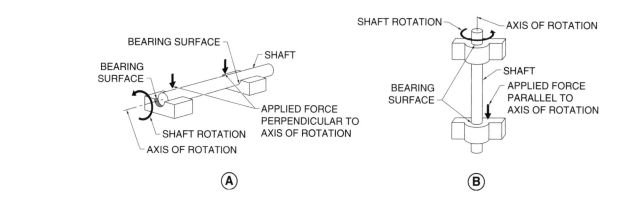

Rolling-Contact Bearings

_____ **1.** Ball

_____ **2.** Needle

_____ **3.** Roller

Ball Bearings

_____ **1.** Single-row radial

_____ **2.** Single-row angular-contact

_____ **3.** Double-row radial or axial

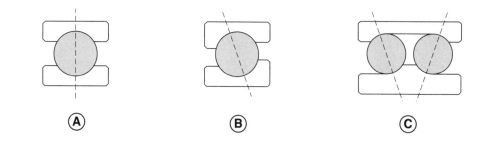

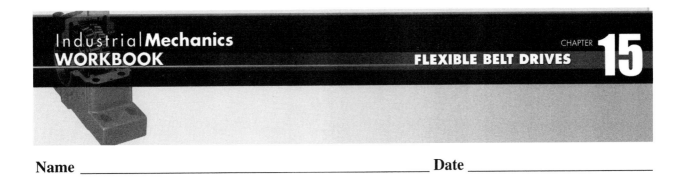

Name _____ **Date** _____

True-False

T   F   **1.** Too little tension on a belt can cause belt slippage.

T   F   **2.** For optimum efficiency, a V-belt should touch the bottom of the pulley.

T   F   **3.** V-belt forces remain constant as the belt bends around the pulley.

T   F   **4.** A fixed bore pulley is a machine-bored one-piece pulley.

T   F   **5.** Pulleys should be placed as close as possible to the shaft bearing to prevent over-hung loads.

Multiple Choice

_____ **1.** ___ misalignment is a condition where two shafts are parallel but the pulleys are not on the same axis.
A. Offset
B. Non-parallel
C. Angular
D. none of the above

_____ **2.** A ___ V-belt is a belt designed to transmit power from the top and bottom of the belt.
A. ½
B. top/bottom
C. single
D. double

_____ **3.** The recommended torque value for a size W hub is ___ lb/ft.
A. 200
B. 300
C. 400
D. 500

_____ **4.** The recommended torque value for a size SH hub is ___ lb/ft.
    A. 6
    B. 10
    C. 50
    D. 100

_____ **5.** Offset misalignment must be within ___″ per foot of drive center distance.
    A. $\frac{1}{16}$
    B. $\frac{1}{10}$
    C. $\frac{1}{8}$
    D. $\frac{3}{16}$

_____ **6.** The proper belt deflection of an assembly using a 6″ pulley and a 3″ pulley having a span length of 12″ is ___″.
    A. 0.046
    B. 0.094
    C. 0.140
    D. 0.187

_____ **7.** The proper belt deflection of an assembly using a 15″ pulley and a 6″ pulley having a span length of 42″ is ___″.
    A. 0.234
    B. 0.327
    C. 0.655
    D. 0.765

_____ **8.** The proper belt deflection of an assembly using a 36″ pulley and a 12″ pulley having a span length of 24″ is ___″.
    A. 0.749
    B. 0.562
    C. 0.374
    D. 0.187

_____ **9.** A trapezoidal timing belt with a double extra heavy cross section is classified as ___.
    A. CC
    B. DD
    C. XXL
    D. XXH

_____ **10.** A trapezoidal timing belt with a mini extra light cross section is classified as ___.
    A. AA
    B. BB
    C. MXL
    D. MXH

_____ **11.** A trapezoidal timing belt with a heavy cross section is classified as ___.
   A. BB
   B. CC
   C. H
   D. XH

_____ **12.** The speed of a 15″ pulley driven by a 36″ drive pulley at 60 rpm is ___ rpm.
   A. 9
   B. 25
   C. 60
   D. 144

_____ **13.** The speed of a 24″ pulley driven by a 48″ drive pulley at 175 rpm is ___ rpm.
   A. 87.5
   B. 175
   C. 350
   D. 525

_____ **14.** The speed of a 6″ pulley driven by an 18″ drive pulley at 100 rpm is ___ rpm.
   A. 100
   B. 300
   C. 333
   D. 400

_____ **15.** A machine is a group of mechanical devices that transfer ___ input at one device into output at another device.
   A. force
   B. motion
   C. energy
   D. all of the above

Completion

_____ **1.** A(n) ___ is an endless power transmission belt with a trapezoidal cross section.

_____ **2.** ___ V-belts are designated as A, B, C, D, or E.

_____ **3.** ___ V-belts are designated as 3V, 5V, or 8V.

_____ **4.** V-belts run in a(n) ___ (sheave) with a V-shaped groove.

_____ **5.** Angular misalignment of a pulley must not exceed ___°.

_____ **6.** ___ is the process of preventing the flow of energy from a power source to a piece of equipment.

_____ **7.** ___ is the process of placing a tag on a power source that warns others not to restore energy.

_____ 8. ___ is the process of placing a solid object in the path of a power source to prevent accidental energy flow.

_____ 9. A(n) ___ belt drive is a mechanism that transmits motion from one shaft to another and allows the speed of the shafts to be varied.

_____ 10. A(n) ___ groove gauge is a gauge that has a male form to determine the size of a pulley and a female form to determine the size of a belt.

_____ 11. A(n) ___ belt is a belt designed for positive transmission and synchronization between the drive shaft and the driven shaft.

_____ 12. Belt ___ length is the total length of the timing belt measured at the belt pitch line.

_____ 13. A(n) ___ value is a designated or theoretical value that may vary from the actual value.

_____ 14. The ___ member is the load-carrying element of a belt that prevents stretching.

_____ 15. A(n) ___ load is a force exerted radially on a shaft that may cause bending of the shaft or early bearing and belt failure.

Identification

Variable-Speed Belt Drives

_____ 1. The variable-speed belt drive is at ___ speed.

_____ 2. Spring

_____ 3. Shaft

_____ 4. V-belt

_____ 5. Pitch diameter

_____ 6. Central sleeve

_____ 7. Cone-faced pulley flanges

_____ 8. Set screw

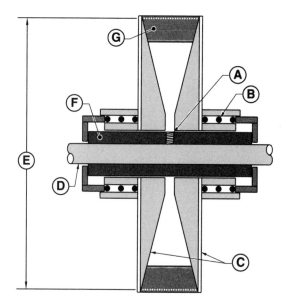

Timing Belt Tooth Profiles

_____ **1.** Trapezoidal

_____ **2.** Double trapezoidal

_____ **3.** Curvilinear

_____ **4.** Modified curvilinear

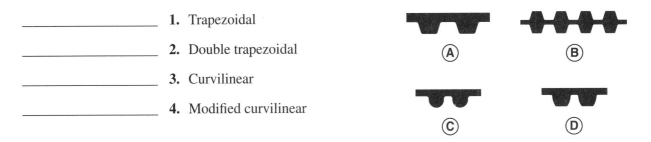

Recommended Minimum Pulley Diameters

_____ **1.** The recommended minimum pulley diameter for a 7½ HP motor running at 1160 rpm is ___ ″.

_____ **2.** The recommended minimum pulley diameter for a 15 HP motor running at 1750 rpm is ___ ″.

_____ **3.** The recommended minimum pulley diameter for a 1 HP motor running at 1750 rpm is ___ ″.

_____ **4.** The recommended minimum pulley diameter for a 100 HP motor running at 870 rpm is ___ ″.

RECOMMENDED MINUMUM PULLEY DIAMETERS*

Motor HP	Motor Speed**			
	870	1160	1750	3500
½	2.2	—	—	—
¾	2.4	2.2	—	—
1	2.4	2.4	2.2	—
1½	2.4	2.4	2.4	2.2
2	3.0	2.4	2.4	2.4
3	3.0	3.0	2.4	2.4
5	3.8	3.0	3.0	2.4
7½	4.4	3.8	3.0	3.0
10	4.4	4.4	3.8	3.0
15	5.2	4.4	4.4	3.8
30	6.8	6.8	5.2	—
75	10.0	10.0	8.6	—
100	12.0	10.0	8.6	—

*in in.
** in rpm

Pulley Misalignment

_____ **1.** Angular

_____ **2.** Offset

_____ **3.** Nonparallel

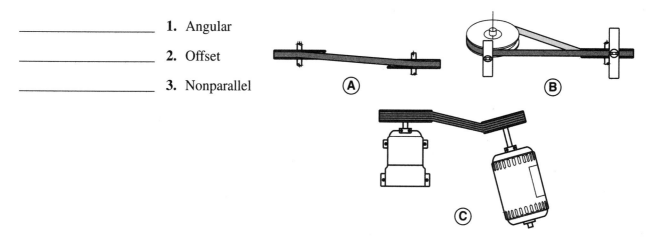

Ⓐ   Ⓑ

Ⓒ

Problems

_____ **1.** The belt length for two pulleys 6″ and 10″ in diameter that are 42″ apart at their centers is ___″.

_____ **2.** The belt length required at A is ___″.

_____ **3.** The proper belt deflection at B is ___″.

_____ **4.** The driven pulley speed at C is ___ rpm.

_____ **5.** The drive pulley speed at D is ___ rpm.

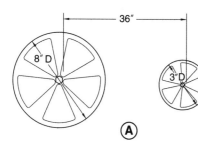

Ⓐ

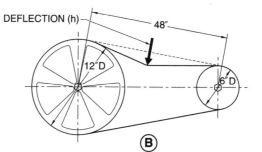

Ⓑ

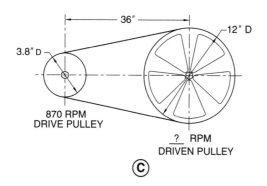

Ⓒ

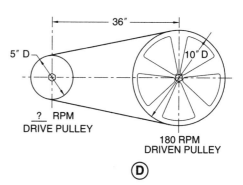

Ⓓ

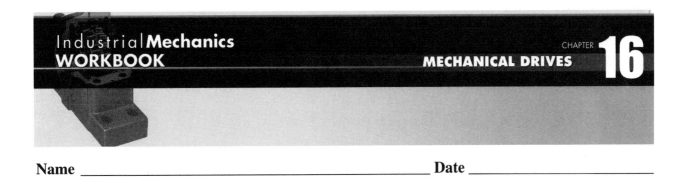

Name _____ Date _____

True-False

T   F   **1.** The colon is the symbol used to indicate a relation between terms.

T   F   **2.** Adding an idler gear between a driven and drive gear changes the direction of rotation of the driven gear.

T   F   **3.** The tooth form of a rack gear consists of two flat surfaces.

T   F   **4.** Backlash is the play between mating gear teeth.

T   F   **5.** Rack teeth are gear teeth used to produce linear motion.

T   F   **6.** Spur gears are quieter and smoother running than helical gears.

T   F   **7.** Under normal conditions, the maximum operating temperature of a gear drive should not exceed 211°F.

T   F   **8.** Gear manufacturers design certain parts of a gear train to wear out or break sooner than others.

T   F   **9.** A pinion is the larger gear of a pair of gears.

T   F   **10.** A worm gear is a gear used at right angles to transmit horsepower between two intersecting shafts at a 1:1 ratio.

Multiple Choice

_____   **1.** ___ is the twisting force of a shaft.
A. Rotation
B. Torque
C. Shearing
D. Bending

_____   **2.** To find lb-in. of torque when lb-ft of torque is known, ___.
A. add 12
B. subtract 12
C. multiply by 12
D. divide by 12

113

_____ **3.** Horsepower is a unit of power equal to ___.

  A. 550 lb-ft/sec

  B. 746 W

  C. 33,000 lb-ft/min

  D. all of the above

_____ **4.** Helical gear drive angles may be anywhere from 0° to ___°.

  A. 30

  B. 60

  C. 90

  D. 120

_____ **5.** A compound gear train is ___ or more sets of gears where ___ gear(s) is/are keyed and rotate(s) on one common shaft.

  A. one; one

  B. one; two

  C. two; one

  D. two; two

Completion

_____ **1.** A(n) ___ is a toothed machine element used to transmit motion between rotating shafts.

_____ **2.** A(n) ___ drive is a system by which power is transmitted from one point to another.

_____ **3.** A(n) ___ gear is any gear that turns or drives another gear.

_____ **4.** A(n) ___ is the relationship between two quantities of terms.

_____ **5.** A(n) ___ gear is a gear that transfers motion and direction in a gear train but does not change speeds.

_____ **6.** A(n) ___ gear is a gear that has straight teeth that are parallel to the shaft axis.

_____ **7.** A tooth ___ is the shape or geometric form of a tooth in a gear when seen as its side profile.

_____ **8.** ___ pitch is the ratio of the number of teeth in a gear to the diameter of the gear's pitch circle.

_____ **9.** ___ depth is the depth of engagement of two gears.

_____ **10.** A(n) ___ gear is a gear that connects shafts at an angle in the same plane.

_____ **11.** ___ is the action or process of eating or wearing away gradually by chemical action.

_____ **12.** A(n) ___ fracture is a breaking or tearing of gear teeth.

_____ **13.** Proportions are either direct proportions or ___ proportions.

_____ **14.** A(n) ___ form is a tooth form that is curled or curved.

_____ **15.** ___ is the radial distance between the top of a tooth and the bottom of the mating tooth space when fully mated.

Identification

Gear Terminology

_____ 1. Center distance

_____ 2. Pinion

_____ 3. Gear

_____ 4. Pitch circle

_____ 5. Outside diameter

_____ 6. Base diameter

_____ 7. Base circle

_____ 8. Circular pitch

_____ 9. Working depth

_____ 10. Line of action

_____ 11. Clearance

_____ 12. Tooth profile (Involute)

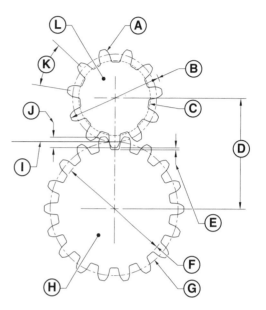

Gears

_____ 1. Miter

_____ 2. Worm

_____ 3. Bevel

_____ 4. Hypoid

_____ 5. Helical

_____ 6. Spur

_____ 7. Rack and pinion

_____ 8. Herringbone

TEETH CUT AT ANGLE TO AXIS OF ROTATION

Emerson Power Transmission

Ⓐ

Emerson Power Transmission

Ⓑ

Emerson Power Transmission

Ⓒ

Boston Gear

Ⓓ

Martin Sprocket & Gear Inc.

Ⓔ

Engelhardt Gear Co.

Ⓕ

Cone Drive Operations Inc./Subsidiary of Textron Inc.

Ⓖ

Engelhardt Gear Co.

Ⓗ

Gear Wear

_____ **1.** Abrasive wear

_____ **2.** Corrosive wear

_____ **3.** Electrical pitting

_____ **4.** Fatigue wear

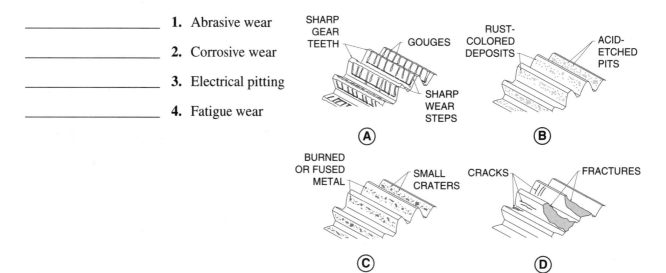

Problems

_____ **1.** A torque of ___ lb-ft is developed when a 75 lb force is applied at the end of a 3′ lever arm.

_____ **2.** The available torque supplied by a 1.5 HP, 1750 rpm motor is ___ lb-ft.

_____ **3.** ___ HP is required to turn Winch A.

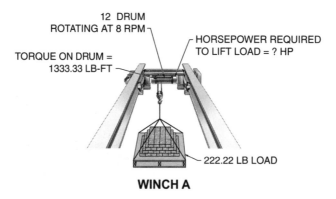

WINCH A

_____ **4.** The speed of a 60 tooth driven gear is ___ rpm when the drive gear has 20 teeth and rotates at 120 rpm.

_____ **5.** Gear A is rotating in a(n) ___ direction.

_____ **6.** Gear A is rotating at ___ rpm.

_____ **7.** A driven gear rotating at 36 rpm requires ___ teeth if the 48 tooth drive gear rotates at 24 rpm.

_____ **8.** The diametral pitch (DP) of Gear C is ___.

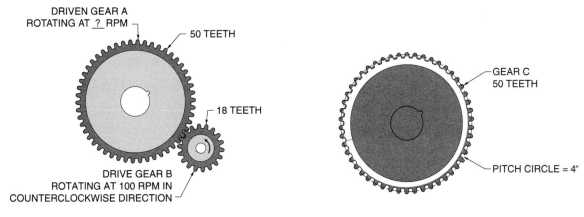

DRIVEN GEAR A
ROTATING AT _?_ RPM

50 TEETH

18 TEETH

DRIVE GEAR B
ROTATING AT 100 RPM IN
COUNTERCLOCKWISE DIRECTION

GEARS A AND B

GEAR C
50 TEETH

PITCH CIRCLE = 4″

GEAR C

_____ **9.** The available torque supplied by a ¾ HP, 3450 rpm blower motor is ___ lb-ft.

_____ **10.** The available torque supplied by a ⅓ HP, 1800 rpm DC motor is ___ lb-ft.

_____ **11.** The available torque supplied by a ½ HP, 1725 rpm magnetic brake motor is ___ lb-ft.

_____ **12.** The horsepower required to turn a 48″ drum at 72 rpm with a 3200 lb load on the winch is ___ HP.

_____ **13.** The horsepower required to turn a 36″ drum at 6 rpm with a 220 lb load on the winch is ___ HP.

_____ **14.** The horsepower required to turn a 24″ drum at 24 rpm with a 51 lb load on the winch is ___ HP.

_____ **15.** The speed of an 80 tooth gear driven by a 12 tooth drive gear that operates at 60 rpm is ___ rpm.

_____ **16.** The speed of a 100 tooth gear driven by a 32 tooth drive gear that operates at 120 rpm is ___ rpm.

_____ **17.** The speed of a 20 tooth gear driven by a 6 tooth drive gear that operates at 60 rpm is ___ rpm.

_____ **18.** The number of teeth required on a driven gear required to produce 50 rpm from a drive gear having 16 teeth at 100 rpm is ___.

Name _____ Date _____

True-False

T   F   **1.** All objects on earth are constantly experiencing vibration.

T   F   **2.** Machines vibrate even when in the best operating condition.

T   F   **3.** A vibration cycle is the complete movement from beginning to end of a vibration.

T   F   **4.** Vibration may occur only from North to South.

T   F   **5.** A logarithmic scale is an amplitude or frequency displayed in powers of 100.

T   F   **6.** Vibration significantly reduces the expected life of bearings and rotating shaft seals.

T   F   **7.** A change in the vibration signature of a machine indicates the ending of a defect.

T   F   **8.** Linear amplitude spectra are amplitude signals displayed in powers of 10.

T   F   **9.** Piezoelectric is the production of electricity by applying pressure to a crystal.

T   F   **10.** The magnitude of vibrations felt by humans is extremely small.

Multiple Choice

_____ **1.** Resonance is the magnification of vibration and its noise by ___% or more.
    A. 0
    B. 10
    C. 20
    D. none of the above

_____ **2.** ___ is the condition where the axes of two machine shafts are not aligned within tolerances.
    A. Alignment
    B. Displacement
    C. Misalignment
    D. Vibration movement

_____ **3.** ___ is the unbalance of weighted forces on opposing ends and sides of a rotor or armature.
    A. Coupling unbalance
    B. Equal rotor unbalance
    C. Opposing forces rotor unbalance
    D. Phase unbalance

_____ **4.** ___ is the unbalance of weighted force across one side of the rotor or armature.
    A. Coupling unbalance
    B. Equal rotor unbalance
    C. Opposing forces rotor unbalance
    D. Phase unbalance

_____ **5.** Vibration velocity is measured in ___.
    A. ft-lb
    B. ft/sec
    C. in.-lb
    D. in./sec

_____ **6.** Displacement is best suited for frequencies between 1 cpm and ___ cpm.
    A. 600
    B. 6000
    C. 60,000
    D. 600,000

_____ **7.** Displacement, velocity, and ___ are all direct measures of the severity of machine vibration.
    A. acceleration
    B. misalignment
    C. speed
    D. weight

_____ **8.** A(n) ___ transducer is an electromechanical device that is constructed of a coil of wire supported by light springs.
    A. accelerometer
    B. displacement
    C. oscillator
    D. velocity

_____ **9.** A displacement transducer is also known as a(n) ___.
    A. oscillator
    B. proximity pickup
    C. spectrometer
    D. vibrometer

_____ **10.** A vibration ___ is a set of vibration readings resulting from tolerances and movement within a new machine.
   A. analysis
   B. foundation
   C. measurement
   D. signature

_____ **11.** An FFT is a ___ Transform analyzer.
   A. Fast Fourier
   B. Free Fourier
   C. Free Form
   D. Front Fourier

_____ **12.** ___ signal analyzers are able to amplify and display signals that are so small they would not show up on a time domain spectra.
   A. Current analysis
   B. Dynamic
   C. Multiple-source
   D. Time domain

_____ **13.** A DSA can simultaneously display a vibration that is as much as ___ times greater than another vibration.
   A. 50
   B. 100
   C. 500
   D. 1000

_____ **14.** Estimates show that about ___% of all vibration problems are related to resonance.
   A. 20
   B. 30
   C. 40
   D. 60

_____ **15.** Estimates show that about ___% of all vibration problems are the result of shaft misalignment.
   A. 20
   B. 30
   C. 40
   D. 60

_____ **16.** Accelerometer transducers can operate at frequencies between 120 cpm and ___ cpm.
   A. 600
   B. 6000
   C. 60,000
   D. 600,000

_____ **17.** ___ is the number of cycles per minute (cpm), cycles per second (cps), or multiples of rotational speed (orders).
    A. Amplitude
    B. Frequency
    C. Velocity
    D. Acceleration

_____ **18.** ___ occurs when a shaft is turning so fast that it attempts to roll over the lubricant rather than squeeze it out of the way.
    A. Oil whirl
    B. Peak-to-peak displacement
    C. Misalignment
    D. Resonance

_____ **19.** An ___ is a device that generates a radio frequency (RF) field that, when sent to the transducer tip, creates eddy currents.
    A. accelerometer
    B. amplifier
    C. oscillator
    D. none of the above

_____ **20.** Transducer placement depends on the ___ of the vibration to be detected.
    A. direction
    B. velocity
    C. amplitude
    D. severity

Completion

_____ **1.** ___ is a continuous periodic change in displacement with respect to a fixed reference.

_____ **2.** ___ is the location (within tolerance) of an axis of a coupled machine shaft relative to another.

_____ **3.** ___ is the absolute value from a zero point (neutral) to the maximum travel on a waveform.

_____ **4.** A(n) ___ is a graphic presentation of an amplitude as a function of time.

_____ **5.** ___ is a measurement of frequency equal to 1 cps.

_____ **6.** ___ is the position of a vibrating part at a given moment with reference to another vibrating part at a fixed reference point.

_____ **7.** The peak value of acceleration is measured in units of g peak, where 1 g is equal to ___ ips^2.

_____ **8.** A(n) ___ is a device that converts a physical quantity into another quantity.

_____ **9.** A(n) ___ current is an electric current that is generated and dissipated in a conductive material in the presence of an electromagnetic field.

_____ **10.** Time ___ is the amplitude as a function of time.

_____ **11.** ___ is the measurement of the distance (amplitude) an object is vibrating.

_____ **12.** A(n) ___ is a multiple of a running speed (rpm) frequency.

_____ **13.** Transducers used to measure radial vibration must be attached within ___″ of the bearing.

_____ **14.** More than ___% of all rotary equipment failures are related to vibration.

_____ **15.** ___ is the square root of the sum of a set of squared instantaneous values.

_____ **16.** Frequency ___ is the amplitude versus frequency spectrum observed on an FFT analyzer.

_____ **17.** A(n) ___ is a device that limits vibration signals so only a single frequency or group of frequencies can pass.

_____ **18.** ___ is a graphic display used for interpretation of machine characteristics.

_____ **19.** Oil ___ is the buildup and resistance of a lubricant in a rolling-contact bearing that is rotating at excessive speeds.

_____ **20.** ___ amplitude spectra are amplitude signals displayed in powers of 10.

Identification

Unbalanced Vibrations

_____ **1.** Coupling unbalance

_____ **2.** Equal rotor unbalance

_____ **3.** Opposing forces rotor balance

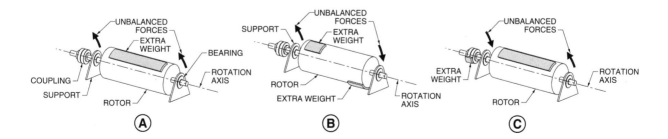

Waveform Spectrum

_____ **1.** Vibration waveform

_____ **2.** Peak amplitude

_____ **3.** Peak-to-peak amplitude

_____ **4.** 1 cycle or 1 frequency in time

Vibration Acceleration

_____ **1.** Time

_____ **2.** Amplitude

_____ **3.** Peak velocity

_____ **4.** Peak acceleration

_____ **5.** Peak-to-peak displacement

Displacement

_____ **1.** Positive upper limit

_____ **2.** Positive lower limit

_____ **3.** Displacement

_____ **4.** Peak-to-peak displacement

Vibration Transducers

_____ **1.** Velocity

_____ **2.** Accelerometer

_____ **3.** Displacement

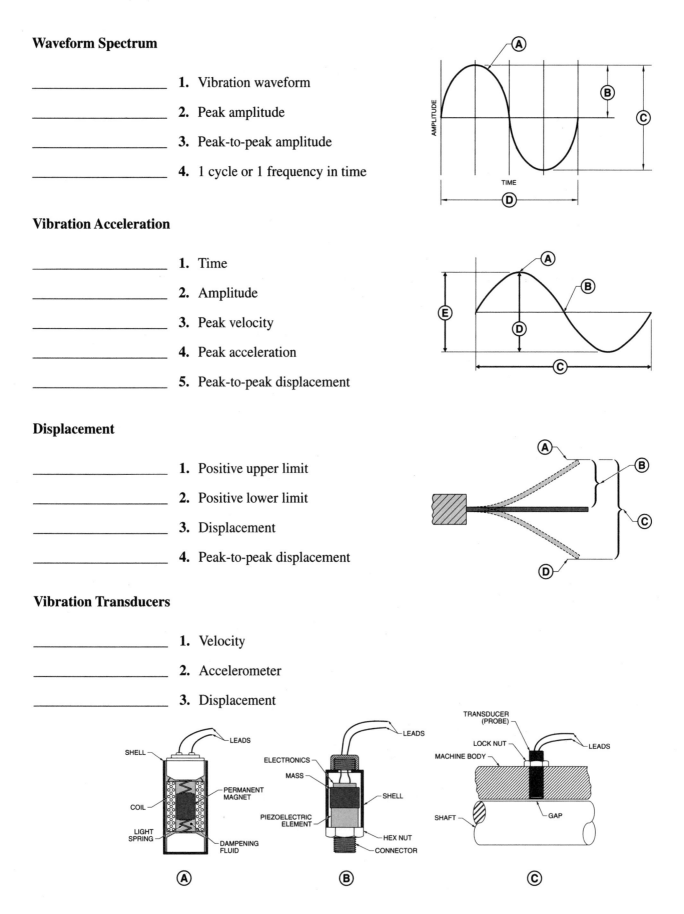

Name _____ Date _____

True-False

T   F   **1.** Dowel effect is corrected by using machined washers 2 to 5 times thicker than the original washer.

T   F   **2.** Jack screws are used for machine movement only.

T   F   **3.** Runout is a radial variation from a true circle.

T   F   **4.** Always choose the combination that uses the least amount of shims or spacers when different shim or spacer combinations can be chosen.

T   F   **5.** The objective of proper alignment is to align the shafts, not the couplings.

T   F   **6.** A spacer is steel material used for filling spaces ¼″ or less.

T   F   **7.** Precut stainless steel shims are recommended for alignment purposes.

T   F   **8.** The two methods of measuring soft foot are the at-each-foot method and the shaft deflection method.

T   F   **9.** When using a dial indicator, readings have to begin at zero.

T   F   **10.** The laser rim-and-face alignment method is used when extreme accuracy and fast alignment are required.

Multiple Choice

_____   **1.** ___ is the process of pressing the start switch of a machine to determine if the machine starts when it is not supposed to start.
    A. Bumping
    B. Skipping
    C. Challenging
    D. none of the above

_____ 2. Shim stock is steel material manufactured in various thicknesses, ranging from
___″ to ___″.
    A. 0.0005; 0.0250
    B. 0.0005; 0.250
    C. 0.005; 0.250
    D. none of the above

_____ 3. When using the combination rim-and-face alignment method, angular misalignment
in the vertical plane is checked by measuring the face of the coupling at the ___
and ___ positions.
    A. 12:00; 3:00
    B. 12:00; 6:00
    C. 12:00; 9:00
    D. 3:00; 9:00

_____ 4. When using the combination rim-and-face alignment method, angular misalignment
in the horizontal plane is checked by measuring the face of the coupling at the
___ and ___ positions.
    A. 12:00; 3:00
    B. 12:00; 6:00
    C. 12:00; 9:00
    D. 3:00; 9:00

_____ 5. A base plate that is drilled and tapped to anchor a machine must be a minimum
thickness of ___ times the root diameter of the anchoring bolts.
    A. 1½
    B. 2
    C. 2½
    D. 3

_____ 6. A(n) ___ is a device that measures the deviation from a true circular path.
    A. dial indicator
    B. eccentric
    C. jack screw
    D. shim

_____ 7. ___ soft foot exists when one machine foot is bent and not on the same plane as
the other feet.
    A. Angular
    B. Induced
    C. Parallel
    D. Springing

_____ 8. ___ soft foot exists when one or two machine feet are higher than the others and
parallel to the base plate.
    A. Angular
    B. Induced
    C. Parallel
    D. Springing

_____ **9.** The shim stock thickness required to correct the angular misalignment in the vertical plane of a pump and motor assembly having a 3″ D coupling, a vertical angular gap of 0.033″, and an MTBS mounting hole distance of 4″ is ___″.
  A. 0.009
  B. 0.023
  C. 0.044
  D. 0.099

_____ **10.** The adjustment required to correct the angular misalignment in the horizontal plane of a pump and motor assembly having a 3″ D coupling, a horizontal angular gap of 0.087″, and an MTBS mounting hole distance of 4″ is ___″.
  A. 0.0261
  B. 0.117
  C. 0.261
  D. 0.621

_____ **11.** More than ___% of vibration problems are caused by misaligned machinery.
  A. 35
  B. 50
  C. 75
  D. 80

_____ **12.** When aligning machinery, MTBS is an abbreviation for machine to be ___.
  A. set
  B. shimmed
  C. stabilized
  D. stopped

_____ **13.** When aligning machinery, SM is an abbreviation for ___ machine.
  A. set
  B. stabilized
  C. stationary
  D. stopped

_____ **14.** Feeler gauges can determine the air gap between two solids to accuracy within ___ of an inch.
  A. tenths
  B. hundredths
  C. thousandths
  D. ten-thousandths

_____ **15.** ___ is a condition that exists when the bolt hole of a machine is so large that the bolt head forces the washer into the hole opening on an angle.
  A. Bolt bound
  B. Dowel effect
  C. Excess bolt body
  D. none of the above

Completion

_____ 1. ___ is the location (within tolerance) of one axis of a coupled machine shaft relative to that of another.

_____ 2. ___ is the condition where the centerlines of two machine shafts are not aligned within tolerances.

_____ 3. ___ expansion is the dimensional change in a substance due to a change in temperature.

_____ 4. A(n) ___ is a device that connects the ends of rotating shafts.

_____ 5. A(n) ___ plate is a rigid steel support for firmly coupling and aligning two or more rotating devices.

_____ 6. ___ is any means of fastening a mechanism securely to a base or foundation.

_____ 7. Good shim packs are ___ cut with each size printed on the shim.

_____ 8. The top position, when using a dial indicator, is known as the ___ position.

_____ 9. A(n) ___ gauge is a flat, tapered strip of metal with graduations in thousandths of an inch or millimeters marked along its length.

_____ 10. Axial ___ is the axial movement of a shaft due to bearing and bearing housing clearances.

_____ 11. ___ misalignment is a condition where two shafts are parallel but are not on the same axis.

_____ 12. ___ misalignment is a condition where one shaft is at an angle to the other shaft.

_____ 13. ___ foot is a condition that occurs when one or more feet of a machine do not make complete contact with its base.

_____ 14. A(n) ___ screw is a screw inserted through a block that is attached to a machine base plate allowing for ease in machine movement.

_____ 15. ___ soft foot is a condition that occurs when a dial indicator at the shaft shows soft foot, but feeler gauges show no gaps.

Identification

Soft Foot

_____ 1. Angular

_____ 2. Parallel

_____ 3. Springing

_____ 4. Induced

Misalignment

_____ **1.** Offset

_____ **2.** Angular

_____ **3.** Offset and angular

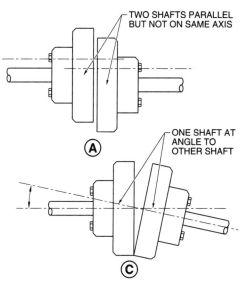

Shaft Runout

_____ **1.** Bent shaft

_____ **2.** Eccentric circular path

_____ **3.** Poorly machined shaft

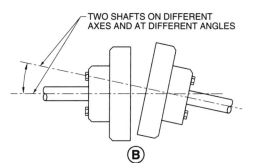

Dial Indicator Readings

_____ **1.** The dial indicators at A show a TIR of ___".

_____ **2.** The dial indicators at B show a TIR of ___".

_____ **3.** The dial indicators at C show a TIR of ___".

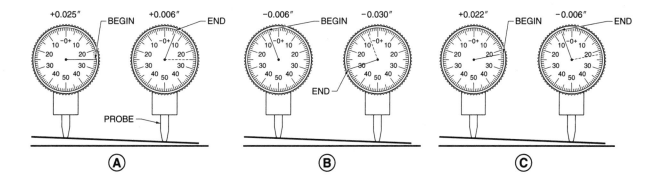

Anchoring Characteristics

_____ 1. Proper anchoring

_____ 2. Bolt bound

_____ 3. Excess bolt body

_____ 4. Bolt bottoms out

_____ 5. Dowel effect

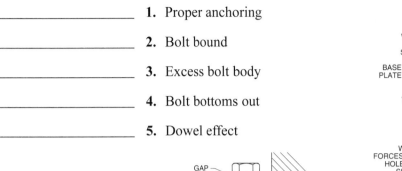

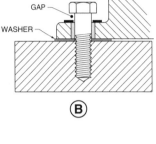

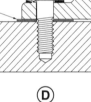

Alignment Methods

_____ 1. Straightedge

_____ 2. Rim-and-face

_____ 3. Reverse dial

_____ 4. Electronic reverse dial

_____ 5. Laser rim-and-face

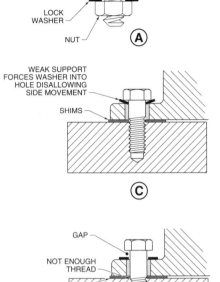

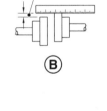

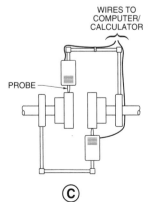

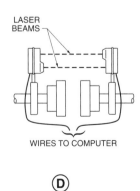

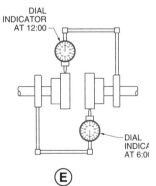

Industrial Mechanics
WORKBOOK

CHAPTER
ELECTRICITY **19**

Name _____ Date _____

True-False

T   F   **1.** Fuses or circuit breakers may be bimetallic.

T   F   **2.** A fault current as low as 4 mA to 6 mA will activate a GFCI and interrupt the circuit.

T   F   **3.** Lightning is the number one cause of fires.

T   F   **4.** Resistance is the opposition to electron flow.

T   F   **5.** A circuit breaker is a device with a mechanical mechanism that may manually or automatically open a circuit when an overload condition or short circuit occurs.

T   F   **6.** A switch is open when it allows current to flow in a circuit.

T   F   **7.** A solenoid is a device that converts electrical energy to a linear, mechanical force.

T   F   **8.** A shock may not be felt if the hands are wet and floor is wet.

T   F   **9.** Whenever possible, work with electricity using one hand.

T   F   **10.** The secondary winding is the power input winding of a transformer and is connected to the incoming power supply.

Multiple Choice

_____   **1.** Common insulators include rubber, plastic, air, glass, and ___.
     A. flexible metal
     B. gel materials
     C. paper
     D. water

_____   **2.** An area in a food processing plant that is used for handling pulverized sugar and cocoa is an example of a Class ___, Division ___ hazardous location.
     A. I, 1
     B. I, 2
     C. II, 1
     D. II, 2

131

_____ **3.** An area in a textile mill used for processing rayon or cotton is an example of a Class ___, Division ___ hazardous location.
    A. I, 1
    B. II, 1
    C. II, 2
    D. III, 1

_____ **4.** An area in a paint manufacturing facility that contains open tanks of paint solvents such as toluene or mineral spirits is an example of a Class ___, Division ___ hazardous location.
    A. I, 1
    B. II, 1
    C. I, 2
    D. III, 1

_____ **5.** The range for most voltage testers is between ___ V and 600 V.
    A. 50
    B. 90
    C. 115
    D. 208

Completion

_____ **1.** ___ electricity is the accumulation of charge.

_____ **2.** ___ electricity is electron flow from one atom to another.

_____ **3.** A(n) ___ shell is the outermost shell of an atom.

_____ **4.** ___ is the amount of electrical pressure in a circuit.

_____ **5.** ___ law is the relationship between voltage, current, and resistance in a circuit.

_____ **6.** A(n) ___ is a device that attracts iron and steel because of the molecular alignment of its material.

_____ **7.** ___ current is a flow of electrons in only one direction.

_____ **8.** ___ is the connection of all exposed noncurrent-carrying metal parts to the earth.

_____ **9.** A(n) ___ tester is a device that indicates if a circuit is open or closed.

_____ **10.** A(n) ___ is a test tool used to measure two or more electrical values.

_____ **11.** A(n) ___ is an electric device that uses electromagnetism to change AC voltage from one level to another.

_____ **12.** Magnetic ___ lines are the invisible lines of force that make up a magnetic field.

_____ **13.** A(n) ___ is a device that converts mechanical energy into electrical energy.

_____ **14.** ___ current is a flow of electrons that reverses its direction of flow at regular intervals.

_____ **15.** Power ___ is the process of delivering electrical power to where it is needed.

_____ **16.** The ___ is responsible for enforcing the NEC®.

_____ **17.** A(n) ___ is an overcurrent protection device with a fusible link that melts and opens the circuit of an overcurrent condition.

_____ **18.** A(n) ___ is an electrical device that protects personnel by detecting potentially hazardous ground faults and quickly discontinuing power from the circuit.

_____ **19.** A(n) ___ conductor is a wire that carries current from one side of the load to ground.

_____ **20.** The ___ winding is the output or load winding of a transformer and is connected to the load.

_____ **21.** A(n) ___ is an auxiliary contact used to maintain current flow to the coil of a relay.

_____ **22.** The current in a 115 VAC circuit that has resistance of 48 Ω is ___ A.

_____ **23.** The resistance in a 120 VAC circuit that has current of 3.47 A is ___ Ω.

_____ **24.** A(n) ___ location is a location where there is an increased risk of fire or explosion due to the presence of flammable gases, vapors, liquids, combustible dusts, or easily ignitable fibers or flyings.

_____ **25.** A(n) ___ device is a device that consists of two dissimilar metals.

Identification

Hydrogen Atom

_____ **1.** Shell

_____ **2.** Electron

_____ **3.** Proton

_____ **4.** Neutron

_____ **5.** Nucleus

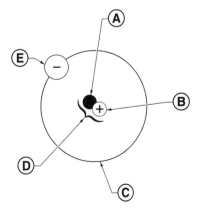

Hazardous Locations

_____ **1.** Class I

_____ **2.** Class II

_____ **3.** Class III

_____ **4.** Division I

_____ **5.** Division II

A. Hazardous location in which hazardous substance is not normally present in air in sufficient quantities to cause an explosion or ignite hazardous materials.

B. Sufficient quantities of flammable gases and vapors present in air to cause an explosion or ignite hazardous materials.

C. Sufficient quantities of combustible dust are present in air to cause an explosion or ignite hazardous materials.

D. Easily-ignitable fibers or flyings are present in air, but not in a sufficient quantity to cause an explosion or ignite hazardous materials.

E. Hazardous location in which hazardous substance is normally present in air in sufficient quantities to cause an explosion or ignite hazardous materials

Testing Contactors and Motor Starters

1. Connect the voltage tester at A to check the incoming voltage.

2. Connect the voltage tester at B to check the control voltage.

3. Connect the voltage tester at C to check the output voltage.

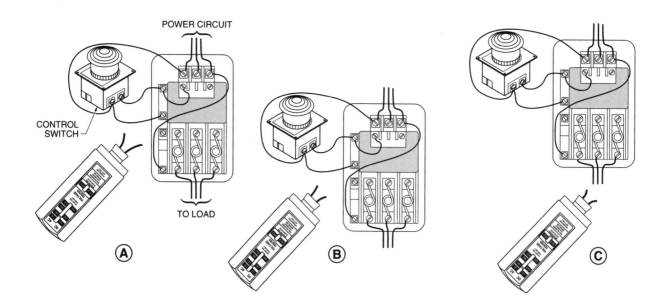

Testing Solenoids

_____ **1.** Reading if coil is normal.

_____ **2.** Reading if coil has a broken wire.

_____ **3.** Reading if coil is shorted.

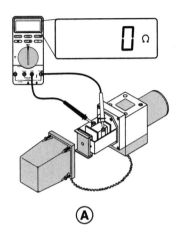

Ⓐ

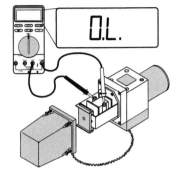

Ⓑ

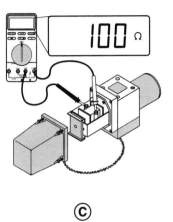

Ⓒ

Effect of Electric Current

_____ **1.** Safe values

_____ **2.** Heart convulsions; usually fatal

_____ **3.** No sensation

_____ **4.** Current in 100 W lamp can electrocute 20 adults

_____ **5.** Painful shock; inability to let go

CURRENT
- 1000 mA — Ⓐ
- 50 mA — Ⓑ
- 15 mA TO 20 mA — Ⓒ
- 0 mA TO 5 mA — Ⓓ
- 1 mA / 0 mA — } Ⓔ

Analog Multimeters

_____ 1. Measure AC voltage

_____ 2. Measure +DC voltage

_____ 3. Measure –DC voltage

_____ 4. Ohm scale

_____ 5. Pointer

_____ 6. Range switch

_____ 7. Zero adjust

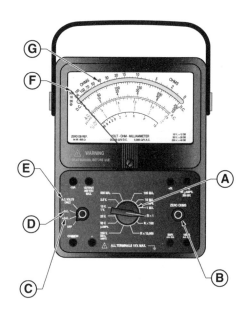

Digital Multimeters

_____ 1. Digital display

_____ 2. Function switch

_____ 3. Measure AC current

_____ 4. Measure AC and DC current

_____ 5. Measure AC voltage

_____ 6. Measure AC and DC voltage

_____ 7. Measure capacitance

_____ 8. Measure resistance

_____ 9. Measure temperature

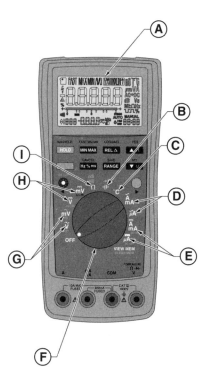

Electrical Safety

Write five electrical safety rules that should be practiced by all personnel working with electricity.

1.

2.

3.

4.

5.

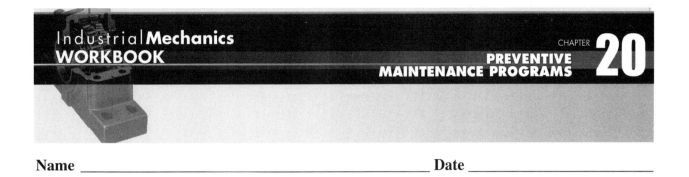

Name _____ Date _____

True-False

T   F   **1.** A thermal imager is a device that detects heat levels in the infrared-wavelength spectrum by making direct contact with the target.

T   F   **2.** In a thermal signature, the lighter the color of the image displayed, the hotter the surface of the object being tested.

T   F   **3.** Ultrasonic analysis is a destructive test method in which mechanical vibrational waves are used to test the integrity of a solid material.

T   F   **4.** Changes in operating sounds, loudness, and/or frequency can indicate developing electrical problems.

T   F   **5.** Continuous energy-use monitoring may be beneficial for some systems, such as those that have large electrical loads.

T   F   **6.** A plant survey is a complete inventory and condition assessment of a facility's equipment and structure.

T   F   **7.** Servicing or replacing a load is a long-term solution when a problem exists with the electrical power system.

T   F   **8.** When troubleshooting power quality problems, some measurements are taken and interpreted immediately, such as those for voltage sags.

T   F   **9.** Ferrography requires taking an oil sample from the equipment to be tested and depositing it on a glass slide that is positioned near a magnet.

T   F   **10.** Loose connections that create intermittent open pathways in an electrical system are the most common type of electrical problem.

Multiple Choice

_____ **1.** ___ maintenance consists of maintenance procedures that involve servicing operating equipment on a scheduled basis.
   A. Routine
   B. Emergency
   C. Predictive
   D. all of the above

139

_____ 2. A ___ goal is a goal that incorporates an action plan that outlines how the goal is to be achieved and a performance measurement that provides goal evaluation.
    A. proposed
    B. specific
    C. measured
    D. standard

_____ 3. A strobe tachometer is a test instrument that uses a flashing light to measure the ___ of a moving object.
    A. speed
    B. distance
    C. mass
    D. dimensions

_____ 4. Ferrographic analysis encompasses ___ monitoring.
    A. wear
    B. contaminant
    C. lubricant
    D. all of the above

_____ 5. Equipment used infrequently, such as disconnects, overloads, and circuit breakers, should be operated at least ___ to prevent them from becoming stuck in one position.
    A. weekly
    B. monthly
    C. biannually
    D. annually

_____ 6. ___ maintenance is basically a series of operating equipment inspections coupled with administrative data collecting and scheduling.
    A. Routine
    B. Emergency
    C. Predictive
    D. Preventive

_____ 7. Manual PM programs are typically used in ___-capacity manufacturing facilities.
    A. small
    B. medium
    C. large
    D. all of the above

_____ 8. A ___ inspection is an inspection intended to establish a reference point using equipment operating under normal conditions and in good working order.
    A. trending
    B. referencing
    C. survey
    D. baseline

_____ **9.** ___ is the organization and management of commonly used consumables, vendors and suppliers, and purchasing records in a PM system.
    A. Plant documentation
    B. Inventory control
    C. Computerized maintenance management
    D. Equipment cataloging

_____ **10.** The main cause of electrical equipment failure is ___.
    A. dirt
    B. moisture
    C. overheating
    D. low voltage

_____ **11.** Infrared thermography is the science of using electronic optical devices to detect and measure radiation and correlating the radiation level to ___.
    A. surface temperature
    B. surface vibration
    C. velocity
    D. mass

_____ **12.** ___ maintenance consists of maintenance procedures that involve reacting to operating equipment breakdowns.
    A. Preventive
    B. Predictive
    C. Emergency
    D. Routine

_____ **13.** A(n) ___ maintenance system is a system used to record and organize maintenance information, which is then used to make the decisions required to maintain the equipment in a facility.
    A. emergency
    B. routine
    C. predictive
    D. preventive

_____ **14.** Power quality problems are found using test instruments such as ___.
    A. thermal imagers
    B. oscilloscopes
    C. tachometers
    D. all of the above

_____ **15.** A(n) ___ is informational documentation created for communication between a technician and maintenance personnel or other relevant parties.
    A. plant survey
    B. maintenance record
    C. work order
    D. entry permit

Completion

_____ 1. A(n) ___ is a series of vertical lines and spaces of varying widths that are used to represent data.

_____ 2. A(n) ___ measures speed by synchronizing the flash rate of a light with the speed of the moving object.

_____ 3. ___ provide specifications and operator's manuals, which are designed for helping end users keep their machinery in peak operating condition.

_____ 4. A(n) ___ is a software package that organizes PM information and automatically generates reports, work orders, and other data for implementing and improving future maintenance activities.

_____ 5. ___ is wear particle analysis using diagnostic techniques to evaluate the condition of interacting lubricated parts or components.

_____ 6. ___ is the planning and action to minimize and prevent equipment breakdowns and lost production time.

_____ 7. A(n) ___ is the first step in implementing a PM system.

_____ 8. ___ maintenance tests include infrared thermography, ferrography, ultrasonic analysis, strobe tachometer tests, and periodic inspections and measurements.

_____ 9. A(n) ___ is a false-color picture of the infrared energy emitted from an object.

_____ 10. The advantage of ___ over other types of PM tests is its capacity to detect a broad range of types and sizes (0.1μm–500μm) of wear particles.

FINAL EXAM

Name _____ Date _____

True-False

    T   F   **1.** An accident victim does not need to provide consent before care is administered.

    T   F   **2.** A personal fall-arrest system must be rigged so the technician cannot fall more than 6′.

    T   F   **3.** Angles are measured in inches or centimeters.

    T   F   **4.** Basic calibration of a depth micrometer requires that the measurement or rod extension start at one.

    T   F   **5.** Typically, location drawings do not include dimensions.

    T   F   **6.** Vises usually consist of a screw, lever, or cam mechanism that closes and holds two or more jaws around a workpiece.

    T   F   **7.** External pullers are used to remove objects such as bearings or bushings from a bore.

    T   F   **8.** The sum of the three angles of a triangle is always 90°.

    T   F   **9.** Polygons are named according to their number of sides.

    T   F   **10.** A hitch is the interlacing of rope to temporarily secure it without knotting the rope.

    T   F   **11.** Torque is the twisting (rotational) force of a shaft.

    T   F   **12.** A crane should be used for a side pull.

    T   F   **13.** Fiberglass ladders conduct electricity when dry.

    T   F   **14.** Fluids that are thin and flow easily have a high viscosity.

    T   F   **15.** Any friction generated in a hydraulic system becomes a resistance to fluid flow.

    T   F   **16.** Tubing may be connected by welding or compression.

    T   F   **17.** A spur gear has straight teeth that are parallel to the shaft axis.

T   F   **18.** The pressure in a container varies as the size or shape of the container varies.

T   F   **19.** An O-ring may be used as a static or a dynamic seal.

T   F   **20.** Pneumatic circuits are generally cleaner than hydraulic circuits.

T   F   **21.** Lubrication generally involves coating surfaces with a material that has a higher coefficient of friction than the original surfaces.

T   F   **22.** Greater force is required to move a body from a static condition than is required to keep it in a kinetic condition.

T   F   **23.** More bearings are destroyed, damaged, and abused during the installation stage than from malfunction during their life expectancy.

T   F   **24.** Vbelt forces remain constant as the belt bends around the pulley.

T   F   **25.** A fixed bore pulley is a machinebored onepiece pulley.

T   F   **26.** Backlash is the play between mating gear teeth.

T   F   **27.** Spur gears are quieter and smoother running than helical gears.

T   F   **28.** Machines vibrate even when in the best operating condition.

T   F   **29.** Piezoelectric is the production of electricity by applying pressure to a crystal.

T   F   **30.** Runout is a radial variation from a true circle.

T   F   **31.** When using a dial indicator, readings have to begin at zero.

T   F   **32.** Lightning is the number one cause of fires.

T   F   **33.** Resistance is the opposition to electron flow.

T   F   **34.** In a thermal signature, the lighter the color of the image displayed, the hotter the surface of the object being tested.

T   F   **35.** Changes in operating sounds, loudness, and/or frequency can indicate developing electrical problems.

Multiple Choice

_____ **1.** A ___ space is a space large enough for an individual to physically enter and perform assigned work but has limited or restricted means for entry and exit and is not designed for continuous occupancy.
    A. restricted
    B. restrained
    C. contained
    D. confined

_____ **2.** ___ is the verification of graduations and incremental values of a precision measuring instrument for accuracy and adjustments.

    A. Tolerance

    B. Caliper adjustment

    C. Calibration

    D. Maintenance

_____ **3.** A ___ is usually one tool with a combination of different measuring devices attached to a steel rule and is sometimes referred to as a combination square set.

    A. caliper

    B. rule

    C. protractor

    D. reversible protractor

_____ **4.** A ___ drawing is a three-dimensional drawing that resembles a picture.

    A. head-on

    B. location

    C. detail

    D. pictorial

_____ **5.** A ___ is a reproduction of original drawings created by an architect or engineer.

    A. print

    B. plan

    C. legend sheet

    D. note

_____ **6.** File parts include the point, edge, face, heel, and ___.

    A. handle

    B. head

    C. tang

    D. blade

_____ **7.** Eccentric circles are two or more circles with ___.

    A. same diameters and same centerpoints

    B. same diameters and different centerpoints

    C. different diameters and same centerpoint

    D. different diameters and different centerpoints

_____ **8.** A polygon is ___.

    A. a manysided plane figure

    B. bound by straight lines

    C. both A and B

    D. none of the above

_____ **9.** ___ is a knitted or woven edge of a webbing formed to prevent raveling.

    A. Web ply

    B. Rebanding

    C. Selvedge

    D. Loop eye

_____ **10.** A ___ sling is created by slipping the loop from one end of the sling over the other end after wrapping the load.
    A. vertical
    B. choker
    C. basket
    D. bridle

_____ **11.** A ___ is the rail and beam on which the crane operates.
    A. cantilever
    B. runway
    C. girder
    D. trolley

_____ **12.** A heavyduty, industrial, 250 lb capacity ladder has a Type ___ rating.
    A. IA
    B. I
    C. II
    D. III

_____ **13.** Ladders over ___′ in height must be secured at the bottom.
    A. 8
    B. 10
    C. 12
    D. 15

_____ **14.** ___ is a measure of a component's or system's useful output energy compared to its input energy.
    A. Rate
    B. Percentage
    C. Efficiency
    D. Value

_____ **15.** A ___ filter is positioned in a hydraulic circuit just before the reservoir.
    A. suction
    B. pressure
    C. return-line
    D. none of the above

_____ **16.** The temperature in °R is always ___° greater than the temperature in °F.
    A. 32
    B. 212
    C. 460
    D. 492

_____ **17.** ___ law states that the volume of a given quantity of gas varies inversely with the pressure as long as the temperature remains constant.
  A. Boyle's
  B. Charles'
  C. Gay-Lussac's
  D. Pascal's

_____ **18.** A(n) ___ is the screw helix of a rotor.
  A. tongue
  B. ear
  C. leaf
  D. lobe

_____ **19.** Lubricants are used to ___ .
  A. reduce friction
  B. prevent wear
  C. prevent corrosion
  D. all of the above

_____ **20.** ___ action is the action by which the surface of a liquid is elevated on a material due to its relative molecular attraction.
  A. Submission
  B. Polymeric
  C. Capillary
  D. none of the above

_____ **21.** A(n) ___ bearing is a rolling-contact bearing in which the load is transmitted perpendicularly to the axis of shaft rotation.
  A. angular contact
  B. Conrad
  C. loading
  D. radial

_____ **22.** ___ damage on ball bearings appears as marks on the shoulder or upper portion of the inner and outer races and will be anywhere from a slight discoloration to heavy galling.
  A. Misalignment
  B. Pitting
  C. Spalling
  D. Thrust

_____ **23.** ___ misalignment is a condition where two shafts are parallel but the pulleys are not on the same axis.
  A. Offset
  B. Nonparallel
  C. Angular
  D. none of the above

_____ **24.** ___ is the twisting force of a shaft.
    A. Rotation
    B. Torque
    C. Shearing
    D. Bending

_____ **25.** Horsepower is a unit of power equal to ___.
    A. 550 lb-ft/sec
    B. 746 W
    C. 33,000 lb-ft/min
    D. all of the above

_____ **26.** A displacement transducer is also known as a(n) ___.
    A. oscillator
    B. proximity pickup
    C. spectrometer
    D. vibrometer

_____ **27.** When aligning machinery, MTBS is an abbreviation for machine to be ___.
    A. set
    B. shimmed
    C. stabilized
    D. stopped

_____ **28.** ___ is a condition that exists when the bolt hole of a machine is so large that the bolt head forces the washer into the hole opening on an angle.
    A. Bolt bound
    B. Dowel effect
    C. Excess bolt body
    D. none of the above

_____ **29.** Common insulators include rubber, plastic, air, glass, and ___.
    A. flexible metal
    B. gel materials
    C. paper
    D. water

_____ **30.** ___ maintenance consists of maintenance procedures that involve reacting to operating equipment breakdowns.
    A. Preventive
    B. Predictive
    C. Emergency
    D. Routine

Completion

_____ 1. ___ includes safety glasses, hard hat, leather gloves, steel-toe work boots, earplugs, ear muffs, welding helmets, fire-resistant clothing, and dust masks.

_____ 2. The ___ is the lowest concentration (air-fuel mixture) at which a gas can ignite.

_____ 3. A(n) ___ micrometer is a micrometer with a digital electronic indicating gauge.

_____ 4. A(n) ___ is a type of drawing where all faces of an object are projected onto flat planes that generally are at 90° angles to one another.

_____ 5. ___ is a method of adding dimensions to a drawing to indicate the geometrical characteristics of an object.

_____ 6. A(n) ___ is a steel hand tool with one end formed to a conical point of approximately 90°.

_____ 7. A(n) ___ is a cut that is made against the direction of the wood grain and is made with full, even strokes at about a 45° angle.

_____ 8. A(n) ___ figure is a flat figure with no depth.

_____ 9. A steel ___ is a metallic material formulated from the fusing or combining of two or more metals.

_____ 10. A(n) ___ is a complete helical wrap of the strands of a rope.

_____ 11. A(n) ___ is a bolt with a looped head.

_____ 12. Hook ___ is the slippage of a hook caused by insufficient braking.

_____ 13. Most metal ladders are normally constructed of ___, which is a relatively light metal.

_____ 14. A(n) ___ is a rope used for hoisting or lowering objects.

_____ 15. ___ is the branch of science that deals with the practical application of water or other liquids at rest or in motion.

_____ 16. A(n) ___ is a quantity that has a magnitude and direction.

_____ 17. The ___ is the temperature at which oil gives off enough gas vapor to ignite briefly when touched with a flame.

_____ 18. A(n) ___ is a container for storing fluid in a hydraulic system.

_____ 19. A(n) ___ is the smallest building block of matter than cannot be divided into smaller units without changing its basic character.

_____ 20. Absolute ___ is the temperature at which substances possess no heat.

_____ 21. A(n) ___ is a device that takes air from the atmosphere and compresses it to increase its pressure.

_____ **22.** A main ___ is the main air supply line that runs between the receiver and the circuits in a pneumatic system.

_____ **23.** Shear ___ is a liquid's ability to remain as a separator between solids in motion.

_____ **24.** ___ is the flaking away of metal pieces due to metal fatigue.

_____ **25.** A(n) ___ bearing is a single-row ball bearing without a loading slot that has deeper-than-normal races.

_____ **26.** ___ is the process of preventing the flow of energy from a power source to a piece of equipment.

_____ **27.** A(n) ___ load is a force exerted radially on a shaft that may cause bending of the shaft or early bearing and belt failure.

_____ **28.** A(n) ___ gear is a gear that has straight teeth that are parallel to the shaft axis.

_____ **29.** A(n) ___ is a graphic presentation of an amplitude as a function of time.

_____ **30.** Frequency ___ is the amplitude versus frequency spectrum observed on an FFT analyzer.

_____ **31.** ___ is any means of fastening a mechanism securely to a base or foundation.

_____ **32.** ___ is the amount of electrical pressure in a circuit.

_____ **33.** The ___ is responsible for enforcing the NEC®.

_____ **34.** A(n) ___ measures speed by synchronizing the flash rate of a light with the speed of the moving object.

_____ **35.** The advantage of ___ over other types of PM tests is its capacity to detect a broad range of types and sizes ($0.1\mu m$–$500\mu m$) of wear particles.

Problems

_____ 1. The area of Circle A is ___ sq in.

_____ 2. The horsepower required to lift load B is ___ HP.

_____ 3. The area of Surface A on Block C is ___ sq in.

_____ 4. The volume of Block C is ___ cu in.

_____ 5. ___ lb of effort force is required to lift the resistance force of Fulcrum D.

_____ 6. The horsepower required to lift the 6 t load is ___ HP.

_____ 7. The temperature on the Fahrenheit scale equals ___°R.

_____ 8. The driven pulley speed at E is ___ rpm.

CIRCLE A

15″

500 LB

500 LB

12′

5 SEC

LOAD B

BLOCK C

B

A

C

3″

20″

9″

FULCRUM D

F_1 = ? LB

F_2 = 1500 LB

F_2

d_1 = 20′

d_2 = 5′

82°

°F

6 T

6 T

4′

10 SEC

36″

12″ D

4″ D

820 RPM
DRIVE PULLEY

___?___ RPM
DRIVEN PULLEY

(E)

APPENDIX

WEIGHT OF STEEL AND BRASS BAR STOCK*

Diameter or Thickness**	Round Steel	Square Steel	Brass
1/4	.167	—	.181
1/2	.667	—	.724
3/4	1.50	—	1.63
1	2.67	3.4	2.89
1 1/4	4.17	—	4.52
1 1/2	6.01	7.7	6.51
1 3/4	8.18	—	8.86
2	10.68	—	11.57
4	42.7	54.4	—
5	66.8	85.0	—
6	96.1	122.4	—
10	267.0	340.0	—
12	384.5	489.6	—

* in lb/ft
** in in.

WEIGHT OF STEEL PLATE*

Thickness**	Weight
1/16	2.55
1/8	5.1
3/16	7.65
1/4	10.2
5/16	12.75
3/8	15.3
1/2	20.4
5/8	25.5
3/4	30.6
1	40.8
1 1/4	51.0
1 1/2	61.2
2	81.6

* in lb/sq ft
** in in.

LEAD LINE FACTORS*

Parts of Line	Plain Bearing Pulleys	Rolling-Contact Bearing Pulleys
1	1.09	1.04
2	.568	.530
3	.395	.360
4	.309	.275
5	.257	.225
6	.223	.191
7	.199	.167
8	.181	.148
9	.167	.135
10	.156	.123
11	.147	.114
12	.140	.106
13	.133	.100
14	.128	.095
15	.124	.090

* based on equal number of pulleys

SLING EYEBOLT CAPACITY LOSS

Sling Angle*	Capacity Reduction**
90	100
60 – 89	70
45 – 59	30
Less than 45	25

* in degrees
** in %

VERTICAL SLING COMPONENT LOAD CAPACITY 6 x 19 IPS-FC CLASSIFICATION* (2000 LB TON)

Rope Dia**	Spelter/ Swaged	U-Bolt	Wedge	Mechanical Splice
$\frac{1}{4}$	.54	.43	.43	.49
$\frac{3}{8}$	1.22	.97	.97	1.09
$\frac{1}{2}$	2.14	1.71	1.71	1.92
$\frac{3}{4}$	4.76	3.80	3.80	4.28
1	8.36	6.68	6.68	7.52

* rates include safety factor of 5
** in in.

SLING ANGLE LOSS FACTORS

Angle from Horizontal*	Loss Factor
90	1.000
85	.996
80	.985
75	.966
70	.940
65	.906
60	.866
55	.819
50	.766
45	.707
40	.643
35	.574
30	.500

* in degrees

SLING ROPE LOAD CAPACITY 6 x 19 CLASSIFICATION (2000 LB TON)

Rope Dia*	Choker	Vertical Load	2-Leg 30°	2-Leg 45°	2-Leg 60°
$\frac{1}{4}$	.35	.65	.58	.50	.31
$\frac{3}{8}$	.84	1.8	1.68	1.37	.95
$\frac{1}{2}$	1.50	2.50	2.96	2.41	1.71
$\frac{3}{4}$	3.20	6.0	6.58	5.37	3.80
1	5.5	10.0	11.56	9.44	6.58

* in in.

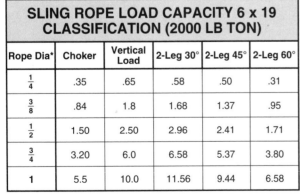

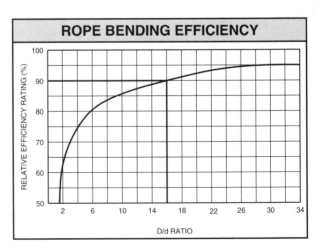

ROPE BENDING EFFICIENCY

WIRE ROPE STRENGTH

Nominal Diameter*	Classification	Nominal Breaking Strength per 2000 lb Ton	
		IPS**	EIPS†
1/4	6 x 19 STANDARD HOISTING FIBER CORE	2.74	–
	6 x 19 STANDARD HOISTING IWRC	–	3.40
	8 x 19 SPECIAL FLEXIBLE HOISTING FIBER CORE	2.35	–
	18 x 7 NONROTATING	2.51	–
3/8	6 x 19 STANDARD HOISTING FIBER CORE	6.10	–
	6 x 19 STANDARD HOISTING IWRC	–	7.55
	8 x 19 SPECIAL FLEXIBLE HOISTING FIBER CORE	5.24	–
	18 x 7 NONROTATING	5.59	–
1/2	6 x 19 STANDARD HOISTING FIBER CORE	10.7	–
	6 x 19 STANDARD HOISTING IWRC	–	13.3
	8 x 19 SPECIAL FLEXIBLE HOISTING FIBER CORE	9.23	–
	18 x 7 NONROTATING	9.85	–

STANDARD HOISTING
6 x 19 SEALE
WITH FIBER CORE

SPECIAL FLEXIBLE HOISTING
8 x 19 WARRINGTON
WITH FIBER CORE

NONROTATING WIRE ROPE
18 x 7
WITH FIBER CORE

* in in.
** IPS - improved plow steel
† EIPS - extra improved plow steel

POLE SCAFFOLD COMPONENTS*

Type	Poles	Bearers	Ledgers (Stringers)	Braces	Planking	Rails
Light-duty** single-pole	20′ or less – 2 × 4 60′ or less – 4 × 4	3′ width – 2 × 4 5′ width – 4 × 4	20′ or less – 1 × 4 60′ or less – 1¼ × 9	1 × 4	2 × 10	2 × 4
Medium-duty† single-pole	60′ or less – 4 × 4	2 × 10	2 × 10	1 × 6	2 × 10	2 × 4
Heavy-duty‡ single-pole	60′ or less – 4 × 4	2 × 10	2 × 10	2 × 4	2 × 10	2 × 4
Light-duty* double-pole	20′ or less – 2 × 4 60′ or less – 4 × 4	3′ width – 2 × 4 5′ width – 4 × 4	20′ or less – 1¼ × 4 60′ or less – 1¼ × 9	1 × 4	2 × 10	2 × 4
Medium-duty† double-pole	60′ or less – 4 × 4	2 × 10	2 × 10	1 × 6	2 × 10	2 × 4
Heavy-duty‡ double-pole	60′ or less – 4 × 4	2 × 10	2 × 10	2 × 4	2 × 10	2 × 4

* all members except planking are used on edge
** not to exceed 25 lb/sq ft
† not to exceed 50 lb/sq ft

SLING VERTICAL CAPACITIES

Width*	Class 5**			Class 7†		
	Types I, II, III, IV	Type V	Type VI	Types I, II, III, IV	Type V	Type VI
1	1100	2200	—	1600	3200	—
1½	1600	3200	—	2300	4600	—
1¾	1900	3800	—	2700	5400	—
2	2200	4400	3600	3100	6200	5800
3	3300	6600	—	4700	9400	—
3½	—	—	5800	—	—	8400
4	4400	8800	6800	6200	12,400	11,000
5	5500	11,000	—	7800	15,600	—
6	6600	13,200	10,000	9300	18,600	16,000

* in in.
** minimum certified tensile strength of 6800 lb per in. of width
† minimum certified tensile strength of 9800 lb per in. of width

ROUND SLING COLOR AND CAPACITY RATING*

Round Sling Size No.	Color	Vertical	Choker	Vertical Basket	45° Basket
		Weight	Weight	Weight	Weight
1	Purple	2600	2100	5200	3700
2	Green	5300	4200	10,600	7500
3	Yellow	8400	6700	16,800	11,900
4	Tan	10,600	8500	21,200	15,000
5	Red	13,200	10,600	26,400	18,700
6	White	16,800	13,400	33,600	23,800
7	Blue	21,200	17,000	42,400	30,000
8	Orange	25,000	20,000	50,000	35,400
9	Orange	31,000	24,800	62,000	43,800
10	Orange	40,000	32,000	80,000	56,600
11	Orange	53,000	42,400	106,000	74,900
12	Orange	66,000	52,800	132,000	93,000

* in lb

ATMOSPHERIC PRESSURE VS LIFT

Altitude above Sea Level*	Barometer Reading**	Atmospheric Pressure†	Theoretical Lift at Standard Temperature of 62°F*
0	29.92	14.7	34
1000	28.8	14.2	33
2000	27.7	13.6	31.5
3000	26.7	13.1	30.2
4000	25.7	12.6	29.1
5000	24.7	12.1	28
6000	23.8	11.7	27
7000	22.9	11.2	26
8000	22.1	10.8	25
9000	21.2	10.4	24
10,000	20.4	10.0	23

* in ft
** in in. Hg
† in psi

SLING MATERIAL STRENGTH CAPACITIES*

6 x 19

ROPE DIA**	Rated Capacities (in Tons)†		
	VERTICAL	CHOKER	BASKET
$\frac{1}{4}$	.51	.38	1.0
$\frac{5}{16}$	.79	.60	1.6
$\frac{3}{8}$	1.1	.85	2.2
$\frac{7}{16}$	1.5	1.1	3.0
$\frac{1}{2}$	2.0	1.5	4.0
$\frac{9}{16}$	2.5	1.9	5.0
$\frac{5}{8}$	3.1	2.3	6.2
$\frac{3}{4}$	4.4	3.3	8.8
$\frac{7}{8}$	6.0	4.5	12.0
1	7.7	5.9	15.0

* improved plow steel/fc
** in in.
† rates include safety factor of 5

EXTENSION LADDER SECTION OVERLAP

Ladder Length*	Overlap*
8 to 36	3
36 to 48	4
48 to 60	5

* in ft

CHOKER HITCH CAPACITIES

Angle of Choke*	Sling Rated Load Factor
120 – 180	.75
90 – 119	.65
60 – 89	.55
30 – 59	.40

* in degrees

FLUID WEIGHTS/TEMPERATURE STANDARDS

Fluid	Weight*	Temperature**
Air	4.33×10^{-5}	20°C/68°F @ 29.92 in. Hg
Gasoline	.0237 – .0249	20°C/68°F
Kerosene	.0296	20°C/68°F
Mercury	.49116	0°C/32°F
Lubricating Oil	.0307 – .0318	15°C/59°F
Fuel Oil	.0336 – .0353	15°C/59°F
Water	.0361	4°C/39°F
Sea Water	.0370	15°C/59°F

* in lb/cu in.

** laboratory temperature conditions under which numerical values are defined

ANGLE POSITIONING

Vertical Dimension	Horizontal Dimension*
8	2
10	$2\frac{1}{2}$
12	3
16	4
20	5
24	6
28	7
32	8
36	9
40	10
44	11

* in ft

FORMULAS . . .

AREA
Circle (Radius)
$A = 3.1416 \times r^2$
where
A = area
3.1416 = constant (π)
r^2 = radius squared

Circle (Diameter)
$A = .7854 \times D^2$
where
A = area
.7854 = constant
D^2 = diameter squared

Square or Rectangle
$A = l \times w$
where
A = area
l = length
w = width

Triangle
$A = \frac{1}{2}bh$
where
A = area
$\frac{1}{2}$ = constant
b = base
h = height

VOLUME
Cylinder (Radius)
$V = \pi r^2 \times l$
where
V = volume
π = 3.1416
r^2 = radius squared
l = length

Cylinder (Diameter)
$V = .7854 \times D^2 \times h$
where
V = volume
.7854 = constant
D^2 = diameter squared
h = height

Rectangular Solid
$V = l \times w \times h$
where
V = volume
l = length
w = width
h = height

Sphere (Radius)
$V = \frac{4\pi r^3}{3}$
where
V = volume
4 = constant
π = 3.1416
r^3 = radius cubed
3 = constant

Sphere (Diameter)
$V = \frac{\pi D^3}{6}$
where
V = volume
π = 3.1416
D^3 = diameter cubed
6 = constant

Cone
$V = \frac{A_b\, a}{3}$
where
V = volume
A_b = area of base
a = altitude
3 = constant

PYTHAGOREAN THEOREM
$c = \sqrt{a^2 + b^2}$
where
c = length of hypotenuse
a^2 = length of one side squared
b^2 = length of other side squared

TEMPERATURE
Converting Fahrenheit to Celsius
$^\circ C = \frac{^\circ F - 32}{1.8}$
where
$^\circ C$ = degrees Celsius
$^\circ F$ = degrees Fahrenheit
32 = difference between bases
1.8 = ratio between bases

Converting Celsius to Fahrenheit
$^\circ F = (1.8 \times {}^\circ C) + 32$
where
$^\circ F$ = degrees Fahrenheit
1.8 = ratio between bases
$^\circ C$ = degrees Celsius
32 = difference between bases

Converting Fahrenheit to Rankine
$^\circ R = 460 + {}^\circ F$
where
$^\circ R$ = degrees Rankine
460 = difference between bases
$^\circ F$ = degrees Fahrenheit

Converting Celsius to Kelvin
$^\circ K = 273 + {}^\circ C$
where
$^\circ K$ = degrees Kelvin
273 = difference between bases
$^\circ C$ = degrees Celsius

STOCK MATERIAL WEIGHT
$W = l \times w/ft$
where
W = weight (in lb)
l = length (in ft)
w/ft = weight (in lb/ft)

LIFTING CAPACITY
$LC = vl \times l \times s$
where
LC = load capacity (in t)
vl = vertical load rate (from Vertical Sling Component Load Capacity 6 × 19 IPS-FC Classification table)
l = number of sling legs (not more than two)
s = loss factor (from Sling Angle Loss Factors table)

ROPE BENDING LOAD RATING
$R_{br} = R_{lr} \times R_{eff}$
where
R_{br} = rope bending load rating
R_{lr} = rope load rating
R_{eff} = relative efficiency rating

D/d Ratio
$R = \frac{D}{d}$
where
R = D/d ratio
D = diameter of rope curve (in in.)
d = diameter of rope (in in.)

ROPE STRENGTH
$R_s = t \times 5$
where
R_s = rope strength (in t)
t = weight (in t)
5 = constant (safety factor)

TONS
$T = \frac{w}{2000}$
where
T = weight (in t)
w = weight (in lb)
2000 = constant (to convert lb to t)

...FORMULAS...

HOLDING LOADS

$$L = \frac{w}{p}$$

where
L = lead line force (in lb)
w = total load weight including weight of slings, containers, etc. (in lb)
p = number of parts

MOVING LOADS

$$L = f \times w$$

where
L = lead line force (in lb)
f = lead line factor (from Lead Line Factors table)
w = weight of load (in lb)

COMPRESSOR SIZE

$$HP = \frac{scfm}{4}$$

where
HP = horsepower
$scfm$ = standard cubic feet per minute
4 = constant

WORKING LOAD CAPACITY

$$L = \frac{c \times wl}{s}$$

where
L = working load capacity (in lb)
c = constant (.21 for sling angles less than 45°; .25 for sling angles greater than 45°)
wl = eyebolt working load limit (in lb)
s = sling angle loss factor (from Sling Angle Loss Factors table)

ABSOLUTE PRESSURE

$psia = psig + 14.7$
where
$psia$ = pounds per square inch absolute
$psig$ = pounds per square inch gauge
14.7 = constant (atmospheric pressure at standard conditions)

CYLINDER PRESSURE

$$P = \frac{F}{A}$$

$$F = P \times A$$

$$A = \frac{F}{P}$$

where
P = pressure
F = force
A = area

CYLINDER CAPACITY

$$C = \frac{V}{231}$$

where
C = capacity (in gal.)
V = volume (in cu in.)
231 = constant (cu in. of fluid per gal.)

PRESSURE OF FLUID IN CYLINDER

$$P = w \times h$$

where
P = pressure at base (in psi)
w = weight of fluid (in lb/cu in. from Fluid Weights/Temperature Standards table)
h = height (in in.)

FLUID VELOCITY

$$v = \frac{x_2 - x_1}{t_2 - t_1}$$

where
v = velocity (in ft/sec)
x_2 = final position (in ft)
x_1 = initial position (in ft)
t_2 = final time (in sec)
t_1 = initial time (in sec)

VELOCITY OF FLUID IN PIPE

$$v = \frac{l_2}{\frac{A \times l_1}{231} \times \frac{60}{Q}}$$

where
v = velocity (in ft/sec)
l_2 = length of pipe (in ft)
A = cross-sectional area of pipe (in sq in.)
l_1 = length of pipe (in in.)
231 = constant (cu in. of fluid per gallon)
Q = flow rate (in gpm)
60 = constant (sec in 1 min)

SPEED OF CYLINDER ROD

$$s = 231 \times \frac{Q}{.7854} \times D^2$$

where
s = speed of extension (in in./min)
231 = constant (cu in. of fluid per gallon)
Q = flow rate (in gpm)
.7854 = constant
D^2 = diameter of cylinder squared

FORCE TO OVERCOME RESISTANCE FORCE

$$F_1 = \frac{F_2 \times d_2}{d_1}$$

where
F_1 = effort force (in lb)
F_2 = resistance force (in lb)
d_1 = distance between effort force and fulcrum (in ft)
d_2 = distance between resistance force and fulcrum (in ft)

RESULTING FORCE WITHIN VESSEL

$$F_2 = F_1 \times \frac{A_2}{A_1}$$

where
F_2 = resulting force (in lb)
F_1 = input force (in lb)
A_2 = area of output pressure (in sq in.)
A_1 = area of input pressure (in sq in.)

EFFICIENCY

$$Eff_T = Eff_1 \times Eff_2 \times 100$$

where
Eff_T = total efficiency (in %)
Eff_1 = efficiency of component 1
Eff_2 = efficiency of component 2
100 = constant (to convert to percent)

POWER

$$P = \frac{F \times d}{t}$$

where
P = power (in lb-ft/time)
F = force (in lb)
d = distance (in ft or in.)
t = time (in sec, min, or hr)

HORSEPOWER
Mechanical

$$HP = \frac{F \times d}{550 \times t}$$

where
HP = horsepower
F = force (in lb)
d = distance (in ft)
550 = constant
t = time (in sec)

Hydraulic

$$HP = P \times Q \times .000583$$

where
HP = horsepower
P = pressure (in psi)
Q = flow rate (in gpm)
.000583 = constant

TORQUE

$$T = \frac{P \times d}{2\pi}$$

where
T = torque (in lb-in.)
P = pressure (in psi)
d = motor displacement (in cu in.)
π = constant (3.1416)

. . . FORMULAS

FINAL PRESSURE

$$P_2 = \frac{P_1 \times V_1}{V_2}$$

where
P_2 = final pressure (in psia)
P_1 = initial pressure (in psia)
V_1 = initial volume (in cubic units)
V_2 = final volume (in cubic units)

RATIO OF COMPRESSION

$$R_c = \frac{P_2}{P_1}$$

where
R_c = ratio of compression
P_2 = final pressure (in psia)
P_1 = initial pressure (in psia)

TORQUE

$T = F \times D$
where
T = torque (in lb-ft)
F = force (in lb)
D = distance (in in. or ft)

FINAL VOLUME

$$V_2 = \frac{P_1 \times V_1}{P_2}$$

where
V_2 = final volume (in cubic units)
P_1 = initial pressure (in psia)
V_1 = initial volume (in cubic units)
P_2 = final pressure (in psia)

PRESSURE LOSS

$$\Delta P = \frac{CQ^2}{1000} \times \frac{14.7}{14.7 + P}$$

where
ΔP = pressure drop (in psi)
C = constant (from Pressure Loss Constants table)
Q = air flow rate (in scfm)
14.7 = constant (atmospheric pressure)
1000 = constant
P = working pressure (in psi)

TORQUE OF ROTATING MACHINE

$$T = \frac{5252 \times HP}{rpm}$$

where
T = torque (in lb-ft)
5252 = constant (33,000 lb-ft ÷ π × 2)
HP = horsepower
rpm = revolutions per minute

CHARLES' LAW

$$V_2 = \frac{V_1 \times T_2}{T_1}$$

where
V_2 = final volume (in cubic units)
V_1 = initial volume (in cubic units)
T_2 = final temperature (in °R)
T_1 = initial temperature (in °R)

BELT LENGTH

$$L = 2 \times C + 1.57 \times (D + d) + \frac{(D - d)^2}{4 \times C}$$

where
L = belt length (in in.)
2 = constant
C = distance between pulley centers (in in.)
1.57 = constant
D = large pulley diameter (in in.)
d = small pulley diameter (in in.)
4 = constant

HORSEPOWER REQUIRED TO OVERCOME LOAD

$$HP = \frac{T \times rpm}{5252}$$

where
HP = horsepower
T = torque (in lb-ft)
rpm = revolutions per minute
5252 = constant (33,000 lb-ft ÷ π × 2)

GAY-LUSSAC'S LAW

$$P_2 = \frac{P_1 \times T_2}{T_1}$$

where
P_2 = final pressure (in psia)
P_1 = initial pressure (in psia)
T_2 = final temperature (in °R)
T_1 = initial temperature (in °R)

DEFLECTION HEIGHT

$h = L \times \frac{1}{64}''$
where
h = deflection height (in in.)
L = span length (in in.)
$\frac{1}{64}''$ = constant (.0156″)

SPEED OF DRIVEN GEAR

$$N_2 = \frac{T_1 \times N_1}{T_2}$$

where
N_2 = speed of driven gear (in rpm)
T_1 = number of teeth on drive gear
N_1 = speed of drive gear (in rpm)
T_2 = number of teeth on driven gear

COMBINED GAS LAW

$$P_2 = \frac{P_1 \times V_1}{T_1} \times \frac{T_2}{V_2}$$

where
P_2 = final pressure (in psia)
P_1 = initial pressure (in psia)
V_1 = initial volume (in cubic units)
T_1 = initial temperature (in °R)
T_2 = final temperature (in °R)
V_2 = final volume (in cubic units)

DRIVEN PULLEY SPEED

$$N_d = \frac{PD_m \times N_m}{PD_d}$$

where
N_d = driven pulley speed (in rpm)
PD_m = drive pulley diameter (in in.)
N_m = drive pulley speed (in rpm)
PD_d = driven pulley diameter (in in.)

COEFFICIENT OF FRICTION

$$f = \frac{F}{N}$$

where
f = coefficient of friction
F = force at which sliding occurs (in lb)
N = object weight (in lb)

Pump Flow*	MOTOR HORSEPOWER										
	Pump Pressure†										
	100	250	500	750	1000	1250	1500	2000	3000	4000	5000
1	.07	.18	.36	.54	.72	.91	1.09	1.45	2.18	2.91	3.64
2	.14	.36	.72	1.09	1.45	1.82	2.18	2.91	4.37	5.83	7.29
3	.21	.54	1.09	1.64	2.18	2.73	3.28	4.37	6.56	8.75	10.93
4	.29	.72	1.45	2.18	2.91	3.64	4.37	5.83	8.75	11.66	14.58
5	.36	.91	1.82	2.73	3.64	4.55	5.46	7.29	10.93	14.58	18.23
8	.58	1.45	2.91	4.37	5.83	7.29	8.75	11.66	17.50	23.33	29.17
10	.72	1.82	3.64	5.46	7.29	9.11	10.93	14.58	21.87	29.17	36.46
12	.87	2.18	4.37	6.56	8.75	10.93	13.12	17.50	26.25	35.00	43.75
15	1.09	2.73	5.46	8.20	10.93	13.67	16.40	21.87	32.81	43.75	54.69
20	1.45	3.64	7.29	10.93	14.58	18.23	21.87	29.17	43.75	58.34	72.92
25	1.82	4.55	9.11	13.67	18.23	22.79	27.34	36.46	54.69	72.92	91.16
30	2.18	5.46	10.93	16.40	21.87	27.34	32.81	43.75	65.63	87.51	109.39
35	2.55	6.38	12.76	19.14	25.52	31.90	38.28	51.05	76.57	102.10	127.62
40	2.91	7.29	14.58	21.87	29.17	36.46	43.75	58.34	87.51	116.68	145.85
45	3.28	8.20	16.40	24.61	32.81	41.02	49.22	65.63	98.45	131.27	164.08
50	3.64	9.11	18.23	27.34	36.46	45.58	54.69	72.92	109.39	145.85	182.32
55	4.01	10.20	20.05	30.08	40.11	50.13	60.16	80.22	120.33	160.44	200.55
60	4.37	10.93	21.87	32.81	43.75	54.69	65.63	87.51	131.27	175.02	218.78
65	4.74	11.85	23.70	35.55	47.40	59.25	71.10	94.80	142.21	189.61	237.01
70	5.10	12.76	25.52	38.28	51.05	63.81	76.57	102.10	153.13	204.20	255.25
75	5.46	13.67	27.36	41.02	54.69	68.37	82.04	109.39	164.08	218.78	273.48
80	5.83	14.58	29.17	43.75	58.34	72.92	87.51	116.68	175.02	233.37	291.71
90	6.56	16.40	32.81	49.22	65.63	82.04	98.45	131.27	196.90	262.54	328.17
100	7.29	18.23	36.46	54.69	72.92	91.16	109.39	145.85	218.78	291.71	364.64

* in gpm
† pump pressure in psi (efficiency assumed to be 80%)

HOISTING EQUIPMENT CHECKLIST

1. Prior to Installation:

❑ Check for any possible damage during shipment. Do not install a damaged hoist.

❑ Check all lubricant levels.

❑ Check wire rope for damage if hoist wire-rope type. Be sure wire rope is properly seated in drum grooves and sheaves.

❑ Check chain for damage if hoist is chain type. Be sure chain properly enters sprockets and chain guiding points.

❑ Check to be sure that power supply shown on serial plate of hoist is the same as the power supply planned for connection to the hoist.

2. Installation:

❑ Install stationary mounting or trolley mounting to monorail beam exactly as instructed by the manufacturer's instructions.

❑ Check supporting structure, including monorail, to make sure it has a load rating equal to that of the hoist installed.

3. Power Supply:

❑ Make sure all electrical connections are made in accordance with manufacturer's wiring diagram, which is usually found inside the cover of the control enclosure.

❑ Make sure electrical supply system is in compliance with the National Electrical Code®.

4. Phase Connections:

❑ Depress the UP button on the pendant control to determine the direction of hook travel. If hook travel is upward, the hoist is properly phased. If it is downward, discontinue operation until phasing is corrected.

❑ Correct power connections if hoist is improperly phased by changing any two power line leads to the hoist. Never change internal wiring connections in the hoist or pendant control.

❑ Recheck operation of hoist after interchanging power line leads to confirm proper direction of motion.

5. Upper Limit Switch:

❑ Raise unloaded hook until it is approximately 1′ below the upper limit switch trip point. Slowly jog hook upward until hook can be raised no further. Lower block about 2′ and raise without jogging until limit switch trips and hook can be raised no further.

❑ Disconnect power supply and check all electrical connections if upper limit switch does not operate, or trip point is too close to hoist.

❑ Make any necessary adjustments.

❑ Reconnect power supply and recheck hoist operation after checking connections or making adjustments.

6. Lower Limit Switch:

❑ Check operation of hoist having a lower limit switch in same manner as for one with an upper limit switch. Never adjust lower limit switch to a point where less than one wrap of wire rope remains on the drum.

7. Lower Hook Travel (when hoist does not have lower limit switch):

❑ Lower the unloaded hook to its lowest possible operating point, or, for wire rope hoists, until two full wraps of wire remain on the drum.

❑ If it appears that less than two wraps of wire rope will be on the drum at the lowest possible operating point, the hoist cannot be installed or used unless it is equipped with a lower limit device.

8. Trolley Operation:

❑ Operate a trolley-mounted hoist over its entire travel distance on a monorail beam while the hoist is unloaded to check all clearances and verify that no interference occurs.

9. Braking System:

❑ Raise and lower hook, without load, stopping the motion at several points to test the operation of the brakes.

❑ Raise hook with capacity load several inches and stop to check that brake holds the load and that the load does not drift downward. If drift does not occur, raise and lower hook with capacity load, stopping the motion at several points to test the operation of the brakes.

10. Load Test:

❑ Load test the hoist with a load equal to 125% of the rated capacity load. If the hoist is equipped with a load limiting device that prevents the lifting of 125% of the rated load, testing should be accomplished with a load equal to 100% of the rated capacity load, followed by a test to check the function of the load limiting device.

11. Filing the Report:

❑ Prepare written report outlining installation procedures, problems encountered, and results of all checks and tests conducted. This report should indicate the approval or certification of the equipment for plant use, and should be signed by the responsible individual and filed in the equipment folder.

12. Operating Instructions:

❑ Issue instructions for hoist operators based on instructions and warning in hoist manufacturer's manual.

❑ Check warning tag or label on the hoist and make sure it stays there. Warning tag is a recent code requirement for new equipment. It is highly recommended for existing equipment. The warning tag should contain the following message:

WARNING:

To avoid injury, do not:

- lift more than rated load
- lift people or load over people
- operate with twisted, kinked, or damaged rope or chain
- operate damaged or malfunctioning hoist
- make side pulls that misalign rope or chain with hoist
- operate if rope is not seated in groove or chain in pockets
- operate unless travel devices limit function; test each shift
- operate hand-powered hoist except with hand power